LINEAR WORLD

Linear Algebra
for Everyone

Linear World – Linear Algebra for Everyone

발 행 | 2024 년 4 월 29 일

저 자 | 김태민

펴낸이 | 한건희

펴낸곳 | 주식회사 부크크

출판사등록 | 2014.07.15. (제 2014-16 호)

주 소 | 서울특별시 금천구 가산디지털 1 로 119 SK 트윈타워 A 동 305 호

전 화 | 1670-8316

이메일 | info@bookk.co.kr

ISBN | 979-11-410-8291-8

www.bookk.co.kr

Book and Cover design by Taemin Kim
First Edition: August 2021

Contents

Preface

Want to be *a super problem solver in just a few hours?* Great! Problem-solving is like a fun puzzle where you find the pieces and make everything fit perfectly. So, it's really about *linking one thing to another* to thrive in the world (see Figure I1).

Problem Solving	1. Links (Relations)
	2. Analysis / Synthesis
	3. Split / Solve / Merge

(a) Art of Life (b) Problem-Solving Trio (PST) (c) PST Puzzle

Figure I. Problem-Solving Trio (PST). The PST includes three key ideas: 1) understanding relations, 2) applying analysis and synthesis, and 3) using the split-solve-merge approach.

Linear Algebra may seem daunting for solving problems. But it's all about breaking a linked puzzle into smaller pieces (analysis) and then putting them together (synthesis). At its core, you'll master the *split-solve-merge* method: splitting a problem into smaller parts, solving each part one by one, and then merging their results to find a solution (see Figure I3).

We'll revisit *linear functions*, the building blocks of linear mappings. By exploring linear functions and equations, you

iv

will lay a strong foundation for problem-solving. Then we'll apply the split-solve-merge method to deal with linear mappings and systems in the same way back and forth.

Biorthogonal Decomposition (BoD) helps us follow a linear mapping back and forth with clarity and ease. BoD breaks a linear mapping into linear functions and merges their function values to compose the result. BoD reveals the orthogonal nature of the linear mapping, offering clear geometric insight to help us visualize its actions and properties.

While Chapter 4 "Quadratic Optimization," marked with a dagger (†), may seem a bit more advanced, don't worry! You can always come back to it later in your "math adventure."

Linear Algebra is a problem-solving superhero, famed for its clarity. The Problem-Solving Trio (PST) excels with linear systems, which have three possible outcomes: *no solution, a unique solution*, or *many solutions*. This booklet begins with linear functions and applies the PST to show how linear mappings work, offering a fascinating geometric view.

By the end of the day, you will master the PST to identify problems, solve them, and check the answers. We'll employ the PST, the core of Linear Algebra, to crack Linear Algebra! Thus, the PST is a powerful tool for tackling problems in the real world. Let's embark on this adventure!

1. Linear Relations

Unraveling linear relationships shows how things connect in simple ways. Problem-solving is a bit like piecing together a puzzle, where you connect the dots to see the bigger picture. Using a relational view, examine how choices lead to various outcomes, picturing them as two best friends named 'Cause' and 'Effect' (see Figure 1). Specifically, explore what happens when 'Cause' is present (forward action as in Figure 1b), and what led to 'Effect' when it appears (backward action as in Figure 1c). Thus, this two-way relationship outlines problem-solving by linking 'Cause' and 'Effect' in a cycle (Figure 1a).

Learning about linear functions and equations is as simple as mastering multiplication and division. They are really useful for solving complex problems. As you get better, you'll see how they connect to geometry and can be used in various situations. Exploring linear relationships helps you understand how things in the world are linked together and highlights the power of a relational view.

(a) Relation   (b) Forward Action   (c) Backward Action

Figure 1. Two-way Relation. It has both forward and backward actions, like a two-sided arrow that lets us move in both ways.

1.1. Linear Functions

A linear function is like a straight line on paper!

Starting from scratch, a (two-way) *relation* connects two groups (see Figure 2a). For a one-way relation, imagine you have a set from, called the *domain*, and another set to called the *co-domain*. A *function* is a one-way relation where each element in the domain is mapped to exactly one element in the codomain (like in Figure 2b). To describe a function, we list all the ordered pairs it maps. For example, the function T in Figure 2b is represented as $T = \{(x_1, y_1), (x_2, y_1), (x_3, y_3)\}$, with the domain $X = \{x_1, x_2, x_3\}$ and the codomain $Y = \{y_1, y_2, y_3\}$. While listing all ordered pairs can describe any relation, it becomes impractical for infinite domains. For an in-

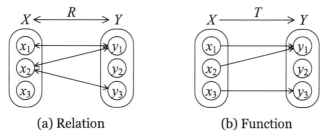

(a) Relation   (b) Function

Figure 2. Relation and Function. (a) A two-way relation (R) may have multiple or no correspondences between two sets X and Y. (b) A function (T) from the domain (X) to the codomain (Y) must have a single value in Y for each element in X.

finite domain, we use a more general description, such as a formula or rule, to describe the function completely.

Suppose we buy multiple copies of a book, and the total cost depends on two factors: the price per book and the number of books purchased (see Table 1). To find the total cost, you can multiply the price per book by the number of books:

total cost = (price per book) × (number of books).

For instance, if you buy three fifty-cent books, the total cost would be one and a half dollars. In this scenario, the number of books represents the independent variable, the total cost becomes the dependent variable, and the book price acts as a constant multiplier. So, the linear relationship between the independent variable (x) and the dependent variable (y) can be expressed as a constant multiple:

$$y = ax, \tag{1}$$

where a is the constant coefficient or *multiplier*. Obviously, the cost of two and three books or five books in total is the sum of their separate costs: $0.5 \cdot 2 + 0.5 \cdot 3 = 1.0 + 1.5 = 2.5$

Table 1. Linear Cost. The total cost of the purchase is directly proportional to the number of books and their unit price.

Independent Variable (x)	0.0	1.0	2.0	3.0	4.0	5.0	···
Dependent Variable (y)	0.0	0.5	1.0	1.5	2.0	2.5	···

and $0.5 \cdot 5 = 2.5$. This illustrates the superposition principle, which will be explained in more detail later.

On the coordinate plane, a linear function is a line that goes through the center point called the origin (see Figure 3). Imagine the *coordinate plane* is like a big grid with two number lines: one goes left to right (x-axis) and the other goes up and down (y-axis). A bunch of points on the coordinate plane is like a way to show how two sets of numbers are connected (see Figure 3a). The *forward action* of a linear function is to map an element in its horizontal domain to another element in its vertical codomain. On the coordinate plane, pick up its spot on the x-axis toward the line, and then move it sideways to reach the y-axis. The multiplier of a linear function determines the slope of its line.

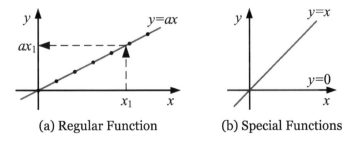

(a) Regular Function   (b) Special Functions

Figure 3. Forward Linear Mapping. (a) A linear function maps an element in its domain to another one in its codomain. (b) The zero and identity functions are graphically intuitive.

There are two special linear functions (Figure 3b). One is the *zero function* ($y = 0$) and the other is the *identity function* ($y = x$). The zero function turns everything into zeros, making its inverse singular. The identity function is the simplest invertible function that carries the same information back and forth with no effort. However, the line graph on the coordinate plane restricts us from showing linear mappings in higher dimensions, limiting us to one dimension.

A linear function follows the *superposition principle*. It means that if you input the sum of multiple values into a linear function (Figure 4a), its output is equal to the sum of the individual outputs (Figure 4b). It might sound complicated, but don't worry — we'll break it down step by step (Figure 4c). We can solve a big problem (big solution) by breaking it into smaller parts (analysis), solving each part separately (small

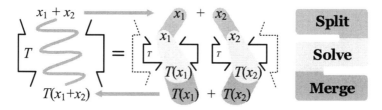

(a) Function of Sum   (b) Sum of Functions   (c) Approach

Figure 4. Superposition Principle. The function of the sum of two inputs in (a) equals the sum of their individual functions in (b), based on the split-solve-merge approach depicted in (c).

solution), and then putting their results together (synthesis). This *split-solve-merge* approach, also known as "divide-and-conquer," is a powerful tool to understand complex ideas.

Let's dive in. Suppose we have a function T that depends on a variable x. We write it as $T(x)$, which you can read as "T of x." A function T is called *linear* if it follows two rules:

• *Additive Property*. The function value of the sum of two inputs, x_1 and x_2, is the sum of their function values:

$$T(x_1 + x_2) = T(x_1) + T(x_2). \tag{2}$$

• *Scaling Property*. The function value of an input x scaled by a constant c is the function value of x scaled by c:

$$T(cx) = cT(x). \tag{3}$$

In short, the linearity condition is:

$$T(c_1 x_1 + c_2 x_2) = c_1 T(x_1) + c_2 T(x_2), \tag{4}$$

where x_1 and x_2 are inputs, and c_1 and c_2 are constants. A linear combination of inputs results in the same combination of their outputs. For real numbers, the only linear function is one that scales the input x by a constant a:

$$T(x) = ax. \tag{5}$$

The additive property suffices for rational numbers to ensure the linearity condition and the superposition principle (see Figure 4). For a linear function, we can break an input into smaller parts, apply the function to each part, and then add up the results to get the answer. For example, splitting 5 into 2 and 3: $0.5 \times 5 = 0.5 \times (2 + 3) = 0.5 \times 2 + 0.5 \times 3 = 1.0 + 1.5 = 2.5$. While this example may seem simple, the "split-solve-merge" method demonstrate its power when we'll explore biorthogonal mappings in §2.4.

Now, let's talk about some basic notations: (a) ":=" means "is defined by." (b) "$\in$" means "in" or "belong to." (c) {} is used to represent a set, either by listing its elements within the braces or by specifying conditions that the elements must satisfy. When specifying conditions, the notation $\{T(x)|P(x)\}$ represents "the set of all function values $T(x)$ where the condition $P(x)$ is true." For example, the set of even numbers, $2\mathbb{N}$, can be written as the set of all multiples of 2:

$$2\mathbb{N} := \{2x \in \mathbb{N} | x \in \mathbb{N}\},$$

where $\mathbb{N}$ is the set of all natural numbers. Listing elements is flexible even for sets that can't be specified by conditions, but it doesn't work for infinite sets. In contrast, specifying conditions is usually complete but might not always be flexible.

We can classify linear functions into regular and singular based on their range. The *range* of a function T, written as $\mathcal{R}(T)$, is the set of all its function values:

$$\mathcal{R}(T) := \{T(x) | x \in \mathcal{D}(T)\},$$

where $\mathcal{D}(T)$ is the domain of T. For example, the function T

in Figure 2b has a range $\mathcal{R}(T) = \{y_1, y_3\}$ for its domain $(T) = \{x_1, x_2, x_3\}$. For a linear function T as in (5), the range depends on whether the multiplier a is zero or not. For a regular linear function $(a \neq 0)$, the range is all real numbers $(\mathbb{R})$. For a singular linear function $(a = 0)$, the range is just $\{0\}$:

$$\begin{aligned} \mathcal{R}(a) &:= \mathcal{R}(T) \\ &= \{ax | x \in \mathbb{R}\} \\ &= \begin{cases} \mathbb{R} & \text{if } a \neq 0, \\ \{0\} & \text{if } a = 0. \end{cases} \end{aligned} \tag{6}$$

By definition, a function only take on values within its range. For example, the zero function maps only to the number zero.

1.2. Linear Equations

Solving a linear equation is a bit like being a detective on a mission. We're trying to find the missing number that creates the known number we have in mind (see Figure 5a). Imagine moving a point on the y-axis sideways towards a straight line and then dropping it down to meet another point on the x-axis. A linear equation for a variable (x) looks like this:

$$ax = b. \tag{7}$$

Here, we call a the *coefficient* and b *constant*. A *solution* is a value for the variable x that makes this equation true. The *solution set* of the linear equation (7) is the collection of its all

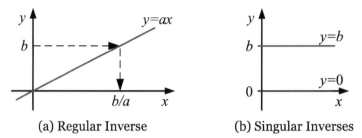

(a) Regular Inverse   (b) Singular Inverses

Figure 5. Backward Linear Mapping. (a) The backward mapping inversely scales the output by the coefficient. (b) The zero function results in singular cases: no or many solutions.

solutions. It's specified by the numbers a and b like this:

$$S(a,b) := \{x \in D(a) | ax = b\}. \tag{8}$$

For example, if you have an equation like $2x = 6$, the unique solution is $x = 3$. So, the solution set for this equation is $(2, 6) = \{3\}$. But when the a is zero, any number works because 0 times any number is always 0 ($0 \cdot x = 0$): $S(0,0) = \mathbb{R}$. On the other hand, there's no solution for x that makes $0 \cdot x = 1$ true: $S(0,1) = \emptyset$, where $\emptyset := \{\}$ denotes the empty set.

The linear equation has three different types of solutions depending on the numbers a and b. When a is not zero ($a \neq 0$), the equation (7) has the unique solution:

$$x = \frac{b}{a}. \tag{9}$$

When a equals zero ($a = 0$), there are two cases depending on b. If b is zero ($b = 0$), all real numbers are solutions to the linear equation (7). But if b is not zero ($b \neq 0$), there's no real number that will work. So, to sum them up:

$$S(a,b) = \begin{cases} \left\{\frac{b}{a}\right\} & \text{if } a \neq 0; \quad \text{nonsingular,} \\ \left.\begin{array}{l} \mathbb{R} \quad \text{if } a = 0, b = 0 \\ \varnothing \quad \text{if } a = 0, b \neq 0 \end{array}\right\} & \text{singular.} \end{cases} \tag{10}$$

This structure is found in various types of equations.

In essence, there are three types of linear equations (see Table 2). It's handy to sort out an equation before diving into it. Consider a linear equation like (7); it has a solution if the number on the right-hand side (b) fits within the range of the linear function on the left-hand side (ax), meaning $b \in \mathcal{R}(a)$. The linear function tells us how many solutions there can be as $S(a, 0)$ behaves similarly to $S(a, b)$ with a constant offset:

$$S(a,0) = \{x \in \mathbb{R} | ax = 0\}. \tag{11}$$

We call $\mathcal{N}(a)$ the set $S(a, 0)$: $\mathcal{N}(a) := S(a, 0)$. $\mathcal{N}(a)$ has two kinds of solution: it has all real numbers ($\mathbb{R}$) if a is zero, or

Table 2. Solutions of a Linear Equation. The coefficient and constant of a linear equation characterize its solutions.

$\mathcal{R}(a)$ / $\mathcal{N}(a)$	$b \in \mathcal{R}(a)$	$b \notin \mathcal{R}(a)$
$\mathcal{N}(a) = \{0\}$	Unique Solution	No Solution
$\mathcal{N}(a) \neq \{0\}$	Many Solutions	

it's just the number zero ($\{0\}$) if a is not zero:

$$\mathcal{N}(a) = \begin{cases} \{0\} & \text{if } a \neq 0 \\ \mathbb{R} & \text{if } a = 0. \end{cases} \tag{12}$$

If b doesn't fall within $\mathcal{R}(a)$, meaning $b \notin \mathcal{R}(a)$, then there's no solution. This idea applies to various intriguing equations, offering you insights in the world of complex equations.

Good to know! Another intuitive way to comprehend a linear equation is by visualizing its linear and constant functions on the coordinate plane (Figure 6). Imagine a linear equation as having two parts: the left-hand side is a straight line passing through the origin, and the right-hand side is a flat horizontal line. Solutions are found where these two lines intersect (see Figure 6a). The center line emerges when the straight line becomes flat ($y = 0$). At times, the flat line ($y =$

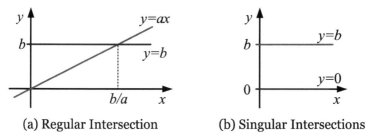

(a) Regular Intersection   (b) Singular Intersections

Figure 6. Intersection of Line Functions. (a) The intersection of two lines is the solution of the linear equation. (b) The zero and constant functions results in an all-or-nothing intersection.

b) and the center line ($y = 0$) coincide or run alongside each other (see Figure 6b). This approach is simple in one dimension but becomes more complex in higher dimensions.

1.3. Geometric Multiplication

Have you ever thought about how multiplication — a basic operation — relates to geometry? While mathematics often treats numbers and geometry separately, exploring geometric connections offers a fresh perspective. Let's dive into this fascinating link between geometry and multiplication!

Imagine a straight line with numbers evenly spaced along its length, known as the *number line* (see Figure 7). This line maps real numbers, placing each at a spot. 0 is, for example, at the center, while 3 lies to the right and -3 to the left.

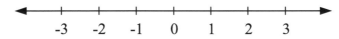

Figure 7. The Number Line. An infinite line marked with equally spaced real numbers.

Let's dive into a geometric construction of multiplication (see Figure 8). Consider two positive numbers, say 1.5 and 2.0, represented as points *A* and *B* on the number line (see Figure 8a). The origin (*O*) and the identity point (*I*) at 0 and

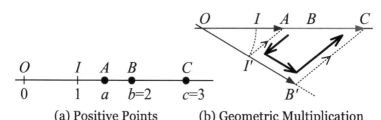

(a) Positive Points   (b) Geometric Multiplication

Figure 8. Geometric Construction of Multiplication. (a) Points at positive values have their distances from the origin O on the number line. (b) Cross duplicated number lines at their origins O and pick a point C on $\overrightarrow{OA}$ such that triangles $OB'C$ and $OI'A$ are similar: $\overline{OC}/\overline{OA} = \overline{OB'}/\overline{OI'}$. Thus, the line segment $\overline{OC}$ is the product of two line segments $\overline{OA}$ and $\overline{OB}$: $\overline{OC} = \overline{OA} \times \overline{OB}$.

1 on the number line, respectively, play crucial role in the geometric multiplication of A and B.

Here's where it gets interesting (Figure 8b). We intersect two number lines at their origins, placing a copy of I at I' and B at B' on the second line. Next, we pick a point C on the line through O and A (denoted as $\overrightarrow{OA}$), such that the line through B' and C ($\overrightarrow{B'C}$) runs parallel to the line through I' and A ($\overrightarrow{I'A}$). The magic happens at point C — this point represents the product of the numbers at A and B. To see this, follow the bold arrows: start at A on the first number line, move to I' on the second number line, swing over to B', and then return parallel to the first arrow, reaching their product at C. This illustrates what we call *"geometric multiplication."*

Let's break it down. Similar triangles, like puzzle pieces, fit perfectly if they are scaled up or down. It's like making a scaled copy of one triangle that matches the other. The cool thing about similar triangles is that the length ratio of their corresponding sides remains constant. In other words, if you divide the length of one side of a triangle by the length of the corresponding side of the other, you get the same ratio for all pairs of corresponding sides. For example, in Figure 8b, the triangles $OB'C$ and $OI'A$ are similar, so we have:

$$\frac{\overline{OC}}{\overline{OA}} = \frac{\overline{OB'}}{\overline{OI'}}\left(= \frac{\overline{B'C}}{\overline{I'A}}\right). \tag{13}$$

From the first equality, cross-multiplying gives:

$$\overline{OC} \times \overline{OI'} = \overline{OA} \times \overline{OB}.$$

Since $\overline{OI'} = 1$ and $\overline{OB'} = \overline{OB}$, it simplifies to

$$\overline{OC} = \overline{OA} \times \overline{OB}.$$

For example, if $\overline{OA}$ is 1.5 and $\overline{OB}$ is 2.0, then $\overline{OC}$ is 3.0.

So, what's the big idea here? Geometric multiplication offers a unique way to understand multiplication through geometry, linking numbers in a visually intuitive manner. This concept extends further in diagrams involving linear functions, simplifying operations in higher dimensions.

The linear function acts like a bundle of arrows tying two numbers from its left domain to its right codomain (see Figure 9a). For instance, the top point in the domain moves to the codomain along the dashed lines, with its function value constructed using geometric multiplication. The domain and codomain are linked while maintaining consistent scaling (see Figure 9b). Two bold arrows represent the unit scales in the domain and codomain. As a value in the domain is a multiple of its left unit scale, the corresponding value in the codomain is the multiple of its right unit scale by the same factor. The linear function transfers the same information between the scaled domain and codomain.

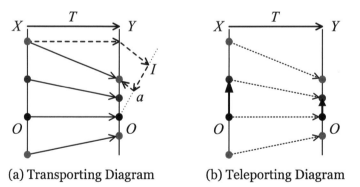

(a) Transporting Diagram   (b) Teleporting Diagram

Figure 9. Linear Mapping in Diagrams. (a) The domain and codomain are graduated in the same scale. Multiplication constructed on the dotted lines adds some complication (b) The domain and codomain are differently graduated to match their ratio.

The linear function and equation together show how they work both back and forth (see Figures 9b and 10a). A linear function teleports the same information from the domain to the codomain with different unit scales (see Figure 9b). For a linear equation, we reverse this process, sending numbers from the codomain back to the domain (see Figure 10a). A regular linear equation gives a unique solution in the domain for each constant in the codomain. However, the zero function maps all numbers to zero. When you try to reverse the zero function, all real numbers correspond to zero (see Figure 10b). For any other constant, no solution exisits.

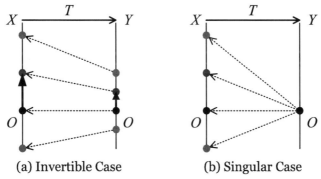

(a) Invertible Case   (b) Singular Case

Figure 10. Linear Equation in Diagrams. (a) The invertible equation has the unique solution. (b) The singular equation has no solution for a non-zero constant or all real numbers otherwise.

2. Linear Geometry

A linear mapping moves a point from one space to another (see Figure 11). If you understand how everything connects both ways here, you can chill out. Otherwise, this chapter will guide you in breaking down a linear mapping into simple linear functions. In the end, linear magic wands will open your eyes to the orthogonal nature of the linear mapping. So, it's very important to fully understand the first chapter.

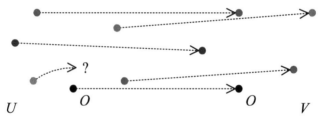

Figure 11. Linear Mapping. Dotted arrows show how points in the input space match with points in the output space, revealing the underlying structure of linear mapping.

A vector space defines where a linear mapping begins and ends across multiple dimensions. It's is an expanded version of a number set in high dimensions. In this space, we'll work with vectors (ordered lists of numbers) for their addition and scalar multiplication (see Table 3). Vector addition is like adding two numbers while scalar multiplication of a vector is similar to multiplying two real numbers. A linear mapping is

Table 3. From Numbers to Vectors. Basic math objects and operations extend from one dimension to multiple dimensions.

Sets	Number Set	Vector Space
Objects	Numbers	Vectors
Operations	Addition	Vector Addition
	Multiplication	Scalar Multiplication

represented by matrix-vector multiplication, showing us how the mapping breaks down a vector into parts and then puts these parts together to get another vector. Like a linear function, a linear mapping carries the same information between input and output spaces using orthogonal unit scales (or bases) in pairs. A linear mapping is broken down into three orthogonal mappings. These orthogonal bases involve a diagonal mapping and two orthogonal transformations, which we can easily understand through using both graphs and math.

2.1. Vector Space

A vector space is like a playground for vectors where they can add and multiply. When you add vectors or multiply a vector by a number, you'll get another vector that stays in the club. Think of it as a group of friends playing games together. As long as they follow the rules of the game, they remain friends and everything goes smoothly. If you want all the nitty-gritty details, you can find them in Appendix A. An n-tuple is a list of n elements, like $(x_1, x_2, \cdots, x_n)$, and it represents a vector in n dimensions. The set of all n-tuples with real numbers, represented as $\mathbb{R}^n := \{(x_1, x_2, \cdots, x_n) | x_i \in \mathbb{R} \text{ for } i = 1, 2, \cdots, n\}$, makes up a vector space. For example, a 2-tuple in $\mathbb{R}^2$ represents a point on the plane (Figure 12a). A 3-tuple in $\mathbb{R}^3$ represents a point in the space (Figure 12b).

In a vector space, *vector addition* and *scalar multiplication* are a lot like adding and multiplying real numbers. The sum of two vectors in $\mathbb{R}^n$ is another vector in $\mathbb{R}^n$ with their element-wise sum:

$$\mathbf{a} + \mathbf{b} := (a_1 + b_1, a_2 + b_2, \cdots, a_n + b_n), \qquad (14)$$

where $\mathbf{a} := (a_1, a_2, \cdots, a_n)$ and $\mathbf{b} := (b_1, b_2, \cdots, b_n)$ are vectors

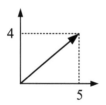

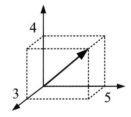

(a) Vector on the Plane (b) Vector in the Space

Figure 12. Vectors in the Plane and Space. (a) An arrow on the plane represents a vector at a 2-tuple $(5, 4)$. (b) An arrow in the space represents a vector at a 3-tuple $(5, 4, 3)$.

in $\mathbb{R}^n$. When we multiply a vector by a number, each part of the vector is multiplied by that number:

$$ca := (ca_1, ca_2, \cdots, ca_n), \tag{15}$$

where c is a constant in $\mathbb{R}$. $\mathbb{R}^n$ is a vector space because $\mathbf{a} + \mathbf{b}$ and $c\mathbf{a}$ belong to $\mathbb{R}^n$ for any vectors $\mathbf{a}$ and $\mathbf{b}$ in $\mathbb{R}^n$ and any constant c in $\mathbb{R}$. Addition and multiplication is special cases of vector addition and scalar multiplication.

The vector operations in the linear space helps us develop a clear geometric sense of the superposition principle. Scalar multiplication and vector addition are intuitive on a plane (Figure 13). Similar to geometric multiplication (Figure 8b), we construct scalar multiplication of a vector in geometry (see Figure 13a). Point B represents a scaled vector of $\mathbf{a}$ at point A by a constant, c. The Parallelogram Law, on the other

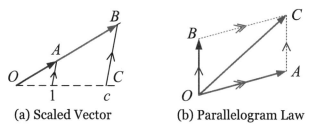

(a) Scaled Vector   (b) Parallelogram Law

Figure 13. Geometric Construction of Vector Operations. (a) A vector is scaled by similar triangles formed with the auxiliary and parallel lines. (b) The sum of two vectors is the diagonal of the parallelogram induced by the two vectors.

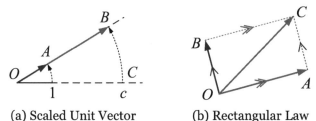

(a) Scaled Unit Vector   (b) Rectangular Law

Figure 14. Simple Vector Operations. (a) A unit vector is scaled using a compass. (b) The sum of two orthogonal vectors is the diagonal of the rectangle induced by the two vectors.

hand, constructs vector addition (see Figure 13b). If we have two vectors **a** at point A and **b** at point B, the corner point C of a parallelogram represents their sum. The vector space thus ensure that our graphical intuition holds true in any dimension. For a unit vector, you can construct its scaled vector using only a compass to match the length equal to the constant c (Figure 14a). When adding orthogonal vectors, a rectangle replaces a parallelogram (Figure 14b).

Let's talk about combining two operatioins on two vectors. It might sound complex, but it's actually straightforward. It's like using two simple operations (Figure 15): multiplying by a number and adding vectors together. A *linear combination* of two vectors, c_1 and c_2, is their weighted sum:

$$\mathbf{y} = x_1 \mathbf{c}_1 + x_2 \mathbf{c}_2, \tag{16}$$

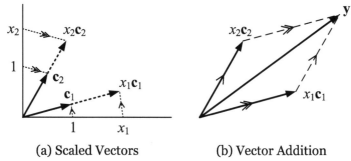

(a) Scaled Vectors   (b) Vector Addition

Figure 15. Linear Combination. (a) Two vectors are scaled by their weights using similar triangles (b) The scaled vectors are added by the Parallelogram Law.

where x_1 and x_2 are the weights assigned to c_1 and c_2. We do two things: First, we stretch out c_1 and c_2 by their weights, x_1 and x_2 (take a look at Figure 15a). After that, we put the stretched-out vectors $x_1 c_1$ and $x_2 c_2$ together (check out Figure 15b), and that's our new vector.

Now, there's something called the "standard basis" with super simple combinations (Figure 16). Think of it like having a set of unit vectors that point in axis directions. When we're working with these, we don't need extra lines to help us (Figure 16a). It's like putting blocks on a number line in just the right places. And instead of using parallelograms, we use rectangles to make it easier (Figure 16b). So, it's all about making math simpler and more fun!

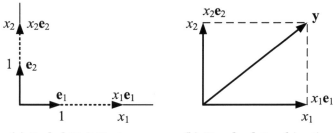

(a) Scaled Unit Vectors   (b) Standard Combination

Figure 16. Linear Combination of the Standard Basis. (a) Scaled unit vectors are located at their weights. (b) The resultant vector is obtained by the axis-aligned rectangle.

A group of vectors in a vector space is said to be *linearly dependent* if there is a nontrivial linear combination of the vectors that results in the zero vector (Figure 17). Here the nontrivial linear combination of vectors means that not all their weights are zero. Parallel vectors, for example, are dependent (Figure 17a). More than two vectors on the plane are

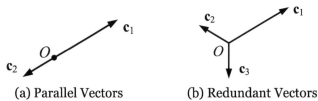

(a) Parallel Vectors   (b) Redundant Vectors

Figure 17. Dependent Vectors. (a) Two vectors in parallel are dependent: $c_1 - 2c_2 = 0$. (b) Three vectors are dependent in the two-dimensional plane: $c_1 - 2(c_2 + c_3) = 0$.

linearly dependent (Figure 17b). If there exists no such non-trivial linear combination of the vectors that equals the zero vector, then those vectors are called *linearly independent.*

A *subspace* of a vector space is a possibly smaller group of vectors under the superposition principle (Figure 18). Now, when we say a set of vectors *spans* a subspace if it has a linear combination for all vectors in the subspace (see Figure 18a). A *basis* of a subspace is a set of its linearly independent vectors that spans it. Notably, the number of linearly independent vectors in all bases of a subspace is same (we'll talk about this in §2.3). This special number is called the *dimension* of the subspace. For example, any two independent vectors in the space spans a plane (Figure 18b).

We have a special math trick called the inner product that helps us figure out vectors. It helps us find useful information

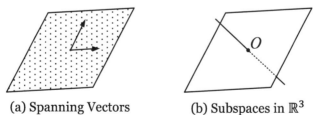

(a) Spanning Vectors   (b) Subspaces in $\mathbb{R}^3$

Figure 18. Subspaces. (a) Two independent vectors span a plane passing through the origin (b) A line or plane passing through the origin is a subspaces in $\mathbb{R}^3$.

about vectors, such as angles and distances. When taking the *inner product* of two vectors, we multiply the corresponding parts of the vectors together and then add all those results:

$$\langle \mathbf{a}, \mathbf{x} \rangle := a_1 x_1 + a_2 x_2 + \cdots + a_n x_n, \qquad (17)$$

where $\mathbf{a} := (a_1, a_2, \cdots, a_n)$ and $\mathbf{x} := (x_1, x_2, \cdots, x_n)$ are the two vectors. The inner product is neat because it doesn't matter which vector we start with – it works the same way with both vectors: $\langle \mathbf{a}, \mathbf{x} \rangle = \langle \mathbf{x}, \mathbf{a} \rangle$. It's like having a superpower to figure out how they are related to each other!

The inner product of two vectors is like lining them up and multiplying the vectors pointing in the same direction (Figure 19). Here's how it works: First, we project a vector, let's say $\mathbf{x}$, onto the other vector $\mathbf{a}$. This means we figure out how much of $\mathbf{x}$ lines up with $\mathbf{a}$. It's like drawing a line down

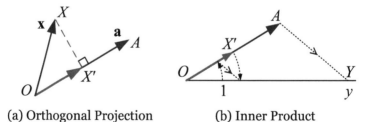

(a) Orthogonal Projection   (b) Inner Product

Figure 19. Projection Product. (a) Project one vector onto the other orthogonally and align them. (b) Construct the length multiplication of two aligned vectors on the number line.

from the end of **x** perpendicular to meet **a** (Figure 19a). We then apply geometric multiplication of line segments, $\overline{OA}$ and $\overline{OX'}$, resulting in $\overline{OY}$ at y (Figure 19b). The inner product of a vector with itself is like computing its squared length:

$$\|\mathbf{a}\|^2 := \langle \mathbf{a}, \mathbf{a} \rangle, \tag{18}$$

where the symbol $\|\mathbf{a}\|$ means the length of the vector **a**. A vector is called a *unit vector* if it has a length of 1.

Now, let's explore the inner product in two easy scenarios. Imagine we have two vectors at right angles to each other (we call them *orthogonal*). No matter how you place them, their inner product is always zero (Figure 20a). Why? Well, if we project one vector onto the other, the result has zero length. The inner product of a vector, **x**, with a unit vector, **a**, gives us its length (Figure 20b):

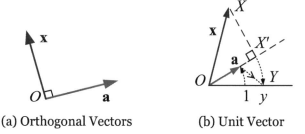

(a) Orthogonal Vectors   (b) Unit Vector

Figure 20. Simple Inner Products. (a) The inner product of orthogonal vectors is zero regardless of their orientation. (b) The inner product with the unit vector is the simple projection.

$$\langle \mathbf{a}, \mathbf{x} \rangle = \|\mathbf{x}\|, \tag{19}$$

where $\|\mathbf{a}\| = 1$. The best part is that when you have orthogonal unit vectors, things get even the simplest. They're like the dynamic duos of the vector world!

Here's a neat takeaway: You can use the inner product to break a vector into simple numbers. In contrast, you can use a linear combination to build a vector from simple numbers. It's like using math tools to break down and build up vectors!

2.2. Linear Mappings

Let's take our journey from linear functions to the next level. In §1.1, we explored linear functions with just one independent and one dependent variable. Now, we're going to broaden our horizons to include many independent and dependent variables. These linear mappings follow the same principles we learned in linear functions. We'll explore how they work with this added complexity and in extended scenarios, offering valuable insights into the linear world.

Let's start with a linear function of several variables, adding together their linear functions. Imagine we have a linear function with n independent variables: x_1, x_2, $\cdots$, and x_n, which results in a dependent variable y. The linear function of several variables has a general form that looks like this:

$$y = a_1 x_1 + a_2 x_2 + \cdots + a_n x_n, \qquad (20)$$

where a_j represents the constant coefficient for the j-th variable x_j, with j ranging from 1 to n: $j = 1, 2, \cdots, n$. We can represent this linear function concisely using the inner product of constant and variable vectors, like this:

$$y = \langle \mathbf{a}, \mathbf{x} \rangle, \qquad (21)$$

where $\mathbf{a}$ is a constant vector, denoted as $\mathbf{a} := (a_1, a_2, \cdots, a_n)$, and $\mathbf{x}$ is a variable vector, represented by $\mathbf{x} := (x_1, x_2, \cdots, x_n)$.

Now, let's dive into many linear functions of several variables. Imagine we have m linear functions of these variables, resulting in m dependent variables: $y_1, y_2, \cdots,$ and y_m. Each of these functions has the same structure:

$$
\begin{aligned}
y_1 &= a_{11} x_1 + a_{12} x_2 + \cdots + a_{1n} x_n \\
y_2 &= a_{21} x_1 + a_{22} x_2 + \cdots + a_{2n} x_n \\
&\vdots \\
y_m &= a_{m1} x_1 + a_{m2} x_2 + \cdots + a_{mn} x_n,
\end{aligned}
\qquad (22)
$$

where a_{ij} represents the constant coefficient of x_j in the i-th linear function that results in y_i, for $i = 1, 2, \cdots, m$. This ij thing is just a subscript to talk about each number in the mapping, like which function and which variable it's in. It is important to note that this is the only mapping that satisfies the linearity condition. As for the formal proof, we'll leave that as an exercise for you.

A matrix handles all coefficients in equation (22) at once. Think of it as a grid of numbers neatly organized like this:

$$\mathbf{A} := \begin{bmatrix} a_{11} & a_{12} & \cdots & a_{1n} \\ a_{21} & a_{22} & \cdots & a_{2n} \\ \vdots & \vdots & \ddots & \vdots \\ a_{m1} & a_{m2} & \cdots & a_{mn} \end{bmatrix}. \tag{23}$$

We call matrix $\mathbf{A}$ a diagonal matrix when all the numbers on its off-diagonal line are zeros. This means that any values in the matrix that aren't on the diagonal line are zeros:

$$a_{ij} = 0 \text{ for all } i \neq j, \tag{24}$$

where a_{ij} is the element on the i-th row and j-th column of $\mathbf{A}$. More special than a diagonal matrix, the *identity matrix* $\mathbf{I}$ is a square matrix where all diagonal elements are one:

$$a_{ij} = \begin{cases} 1 \text{ if } i = j \\ 0 \text{ if } i \neq j. \end{cases} \tag{25}$$

Let $\mathbb{R}^{m \times n}$ be the collection of all $m \times n$ matrices with m rows and n columns of elements from $\mathbb{R}$. $\mathbb{R}^{1 \times n}$ and $\mathbb{R}^{m \times 1}$ (or just $\mathbb{R}^m$) represent sets of row and column vectors, respectively.

The *transpose* of the matrix $\mathbf{A}$, denoted as $\mathbf{A}^T$, is another matrix in $\mathbb{R}^{n \times m}$ that swaps its rows and columns, like this:

$$\mathbf{A}^T := \begin{bmatrix} a_{11} & a_{21} & \cdots & a_{m1} \\ a_{12} & a_{22} & \cdots & a_{m2} \\ \vdots & \vdots & \ddots & \vdots \\ a_{1n} & a_{n2} & \cdots & a_{nm} \end{bmatrix}. \tag{26}$$

It's like flipping the matrix. We call a matrix *symmetric* when it's the same as its transpose:

$$\mathbf{A}^T = \mathbf{A}. \tag{27}$$

A symmetric matric is always square, which means it has the same number of rows and columns.

When we multiply two matrices, we take the inner products of each row in the first matrix with each column in the second matrix as shown in Figure 21:

$$\mathbf{Y} = \mathbf{AX}, \tag{28}$$

where $\mathbf{A}$ is a matrix with m rows and n columns ($\mathbf{A} \in \mathbb{R}^{m \times n}$), $\mathbf{X}$ is a matrix with n rows and l columns ($\mathbf{X} \in \mathbb{R}^{n \times l}$), and $\mathbf{Y}$ is a matrix with m rows and l columns ($\mathbf{Y} \in \mathbb{R}^{m \times l}$). We obtain each number y_{ik} in $\mathbf{Y}$ using the inner product formula:

$$y_{ik} := \langle \mathbf{a}_i, \mathbf{x}_k \rangle,$$

where $\mathbf{a}_i$ is the i-th row vector of $\mathbf{A}$ and $\mathbf{x}_k$ is the k-th column vector of $\mathbf{X}$.

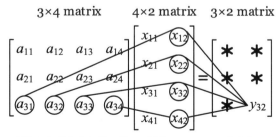

Figure 21. Matrix Multiplication. When you multiply a 3×4 matrix by a 4×2 matrix, you get a 3×2 matrix [1].

Let's see some basic properties of matrix multiplication. It's associative, meaning that for three matrices $\mathbf{A}$, $\mathbf{B}$, and $\mathbf{C}$, $(\mathbf{AB})\mathbf{C}$ is identical to $\mathbf{A}(\mathbf{BC})$: $(\mathbf{AB})\mathbf{C} = \mathbf{A}(\mathbf{BC})$. However, it's not commutative, so $\mathbf{AB}$ is not equal to $\mathbf{BA}$: $\mathbf{AB} \neq \mathbf{BA}$. You can try to prove this yourself! The identity matrix doesn't change a matrix when you multiply it from the left or right. So, $\mathbf{AI}$ is equal to $\mathbf{A}$ ($\mathbf{AI} = \mathbf{A}$), and $\mathbf{IA}$ is also equal to $\mathbf{A}$ ($\mathbf{IA} = \mathbf{A}$). When you multiply two matrices, the transpose of their product is the reverse multiplication of their transposes:

$$(\mathbf{AX})^T = \mathbf{X}^T \mathbf{A}^T. \tag{29}$$

For two column vectors $\mathbf{a}$ and $\mathbf{x}$ in $\mathbb{R}^n$, $\langle \mathbf{a}, \mathbf{x} \rangle = \mathbf{a}^T \mathbf{x}$.

Now, let's make things simple. The matrix-vector multiplication succinctly represents a linear mapping like (1):

$$\mathbf{y} = \mathbf{Ax}, \tag{30}$$

where $\mathbf{A} \in \mathbb{R}^{m \times n}$ is a coefficient matrix, $\mathbf{x} \in \mathbb{R}^n$ is an independent vector, and $\mathbf{y} \in \mathbb{R}^m$ is a dependent vector. This linear mapping takes a vector from the domain in $\mathbb{R}^n$ and send it to the codomain in $\mathbb{R}^m$ as depicted in Figure 22a.

A *linear transformation* is a special case of a linear mapping where the domain and codomain are the same (as seen Figure 22b). A symmetric matrix can represent such a linear transformation. For example, both inner and outer squares of a matrix are symmetric (see Figure 23). For a matrix $\mathbf{A}$, its

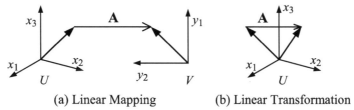

(a) Linear Mapping　　　　(b) Linear Transformation

Figure 22. Linear Mapping and Transformation. (a) A linear mapping takes a point from the domain U to another point in the codomain V. (b) A linear transformation moves a point to another point within the same vector space.

inner square, $\mathbf{A}^T\mathbf{A}$, induces a linear transformation in the domain of $\mathbf{A}$, while its outer square, $\mathbf{A}\mathbf{A}^T$, induces another one in the codomain of $\mathbf{A}$.

Welcome to the steepest hill of the linear world! From the top, matrix-vector multiplication unveils two essential facets of a linear mapping: analytic and synthetic actions. A matrix consists of either row or column vectors (see Table 4). Let's

$$\begin{bmatrix} \mathbf{A}^T \end{bmatrix}\begin{bmatrix} \mathbf{A} \end{bmatrix} = \begin{bmatrix} \mathbf{A}^T\mathbf{A} \end{bmatrix} \qquad \begin{bmatrix} \mathbf{A} \end{bmatrix}\begin{bmatrix} \mathbf{A}^T \end{bmatrix} = \begin{bmatrix} \mathbf{A}\mathbf{A}^T \end{bmatrix}$$

(a) Inner Square　　　　(b) Outer Square

Figure 23. Square Matrices. (a) The inner square of a matrix is a square matrix with the same width. (b) The outer square of a matrix is a square matrix with the same height.

define $\mathbf{r}_i := [a_{i1}\ a_{i2}\ \cdots\ a_{in}]$ and $\mathbf{c}_j := [a_{1j}\ a_{2j}\ \cdots\ a_{mj}]^T$ as the i-th row and j-th column vectors of the matrix $\mathbf{A}$, respectively:

$$\mathbf{A} = \begin{bmatrix} \mathbf{r}_1 \\ \mathbf{r}_2 \\ \vdots \\ \mathbf{r}_m \end{bmatrix} \tag{31}$$

$$= [\mathbf{c}_1\ \mathbf{c}_2\ \cdots\ \mathbf{c}_n]$$

So, there are two ways to multiply a matrix and vector: (a) it gathers inner products of $\mathbf{A}$'s row vectors with $\mathbf{x}$ into $\mathbf{y}$, or (b) it forms a linear combination of $\mathbf{A}$'s column vectors by $\mathbf{x}$ to composes $\mathbf{y}$ (see Figure 24). The analytic action of a linear mapping involves inner products of $\mathbf{A}$'s row vectors — $\mathbf{r}_1, \mathbf{r}_2,$ $\cdots, \mathbf{r}_m$ — with the independent vector $\mathbf{x}$ one by one as shown

Table 4. The Two Faces of a Matrix. A rectangular matrix is a collection of either row or column vectors.

Vectors	$\mathbf{c}_1$	$\mathbf{c}_2$	$\cdots$	$\mathbf{c}_j$	$\cdots$	$\mathbf{c}_n$
$\mathbf{r}_1$	a_{11}	a_{12}	$\cdots$	a_{1j}	$\cdots$	a_{1n}
$\mathbf{r}_2$	a_{21}	a_{22}		a_{2j}		a_{2n}
$\vdots$	$\vdots$		$\ddots$			$\vdots$
$\mathbf{r}_i$	a_{i1}	a_{i2}		a_{ij}		a_{in}
$\vdots$	$\vdots$				$\ddots$	$\vdots$
$\mathbf{r}_m$	a_{m1}	a_{m2}	$\cdots$	a_{mj}	$\cdots$	a_{mn}

in Figure 24a. It's like casting a shadow of $\mathbf{x}$ onto each axis of row vectors. These indivisual shadows are stacked into $\mathbf{y}$:

$$
\mathbf{y} = \begin{bmatrix} \mathbf{r}_1 \\ \mathbf{r}_2 \\ \vdots \\ \mathbf{r}_m \end{bmatrix} \mathbf{x} \\
= \begin{bmatrix} \mathbf{r}_1 \mathbf{x} \\ \mathbf{r}_2 \mathbf{x} \\ \vdots \\ \mathbf{r}_m \mathbf{x} \end{bmatrix}.
$$

(32)

In contrast, the synthetic action of the linear mapping needs a linear combination of $\mathbf{A}$'s column vectors — $\mathbf{c}_1, \mathbf{c}_2, \cdots, \mathbf{c}_n$ — with the independent variables $x_1, x_2, \cdots, x_n$ from $\mathbf{x}$, as shown in Figure 24b. This is like assembling $\mathbf{y}$ by combining

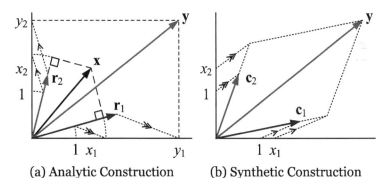

(a) Analytic Construction   (b) Synthetic Construction

Figure 24. Two Linear Constructions. (a) The inner products of $\mathbf{x}$ with $\mathbf{r}_1$ and $\mathbf{r}_2$ result in the vector $\mathbf{y}$. (b) A linear combination of $\mathbf{c}_1$ and $\mathbf{c}_2$ with $\mathbf{x}$ also result in the vector $\mathbf{y}$.

pieces from each column vector, guided by the values in $\mathbf{x}$:

$$\begin{aligned}
\mathbf{y} &= [\mathbf{c}_1 \ \mathbf{c}_2 \ \cdots \ \mathbf{c}_n]\mathbf{x} \\
&= \mathbf{c}_1 x_1 + \mathbf{c}_2 x_2 + \cdots + \mathbf{c}_n x_n \\
&= x_1 \mathbf{c}_1 + x_2 \mathbf{c}_2 + \cdots + x_n \mathbf{c}_n.
\end{aligned} \tag{33}$$

Both the analytic and synthetic actions of the linear mapping may appear complex even in the plane. No worries! Orthogonal mappings offer the easiest way to both break down and compose linear mappings (see §2.3 and 2.4).

2.3. Orthogonal Mappings

Welcome to the world of right angles! Most linear mappings are tricky to grasp because they involve all sorts of angles in their matrices, much like the natural world. However, there's something like modern skyscrapers — simple, powerful, and crystal clear in what they do. They're called *orthogonal mappings*! What makes them special is their love for right angles. In an orthogonal mapping, all vectors in its matrix are like best friends who stand at right angles to each other (see Figure 25). Orthogonal mappings are like a treasure in the mapping world, making math more fun and easier!

Formally, we call a linear mapping *orthogonal* when the row vectors in its matrix are perpendicular to each other, and the same holds true for the column vectors. Using the matrix

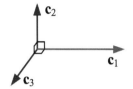
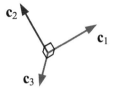

(a) Axis-aligned Vectors   (b) Orthogonal Vectors

Figure 25. Vectors at Right Angles. (a) A sparse diagonal matrix represents axis-aligned vectors. (b) A dense orthogonal matrix represents orthogonal unit vectors.

defined in Table 4, we find that $\mathbf{r}_i^T \mathbf{r}_k = 0$ and $\mathbf{c}_i^T \mathbf{c}_k = 0$ for $i \neq k$. There are two distinctive types of orthogonal mappings: diagonal mapping and orthogonal transformation. As their names imply, a diagonal matrix represents the former while a special matrix called an orthogonal matrix represents the latter. When it comes to non-zero elements, a diagonal matrix is sparse only on its diagonal line while an orthogonal matrix is populated everywhere, as shown in Figure 26.

$$\mathbf{A} = \begin{bmatrix} 2 & 0 & 0 \\ 0 & 1 & 0 \\ 0 & 0 & 3 \end{bmatrix} \qquad \mathbf{A} = \begin{bmatrix} 0.80 & 0.48 & -0.36 \\ -0.60 & 0.64 & -0.48 \\ 0.00 & 0.60 & 0.80 \end{bmatrix}$$

(a) Diagonal Matrix   (b) Orthogonal Matrix

Figure 26. Diagonal and Orthogonal Matrices. (a) A diagonal matrix has a few non-zero elements on the diagonal. (b) In contrast, an orthogonal matrix has many non-zero elements.

The simplest orthogonal mapping is a *diagonal mapping*. It deals with each independent and variables separately. In fact, a diagonal mapping is a group of linear functions that a diagonal matrix can represent. Let's explore this with an example involving two linear functions:

$$y_1 = 2x_1$$
$$y_2 = 0.5x_2. \tag{34}$$

The first linear function scales up the first independent variable x_1, by a factor of 2 while the second one scales down another variable x_2, by half (Figure 27). These two functions are represented using a square diagonal matrix:

$$\begin{bmatrix} y_1 \\ y_2 \end{bmatrix} = \begin{bmatrix} 2.0 & 0.0 \\ 0.0 & 0.5 \end{bmatrix} \begin{bmatrix} x_1 \\ x_2 \end{bmatrix}. \tag{35}$$

Now, what if we have more variables? A short wide diagonal matrix pads extra independent variables redundantly:

$$\begin{bmatrix} y_1 \\ y_2 \end{bmatrix} = \begin{bmatrix} 2.0 & 0.0 & 0.0 \\ 0.0 & 0.5 & 0.0 \end{bmatrix} \begin{bmatrix} x_1 \\ x_2 \\ x_3 \end{bmatrix}. \tag{36}$$

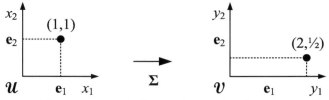

Figure 27. Eigen Heaven. A diagonal mapping does its magic by individually tweaking each part of a vector to match another.

A tall diagonal matrix pads dependent variables with zeros:

$$\begin{bmatrix} y_1 \\ y_2 \\ y_3 \end{bmatrix} = \begin{bmatrix} 2.0 & 0.0 \\ 0.0 & 0.5 \\ 0.0 & 0.0 \end{bmatrix} \begin{bmatrix} x_1 \\ x_2 \end{bmatrix}. \tag{37}$$

Practically, these three diagonal matrices are equivalent because they only involve nontrivial mapping for the first two variables. A diagonal mapping is simple to understand, even in high dimensions, as we can handle each elementary linear mapping separately. Geometrically, it's like resizing an independent vector along its axes to compute its dependent vector. This mathematical world is called *Eigen heaven* because everything works straightly with one-to-one relationships.

Another orthogonal mapping is the orthogonal transformation. A linear transformation is called *orthogonal* if it keeps all inner products unchanged in a vector space:

$$\langle T\mathbf{a}, T\mathbf{x} \rangle = \langle \mathbf{a}, \mathbf{x} \rangle, \tag{38}$$

where T is the orthogonal transformation, and $\mathbf{a}$ and $\mathbf{x}$ are any vectors in the space. We call the square matrix, $\mathbf{Q}$, representing T, an *orthogonal matrix* due to its magical properties:

$$\mathbf{Q}^T \mathbf{Q} = \mathbf{I}. \tag{39}$$

Because it has to preserve all inner products by definition:

$$\mathbf{a}^T \mathbf{Q}^T \mathbf{Q} \mathbf{x} = \mathbf{a}^T \mathbf{x}, \tag{40}$$

for any vectors $\mathbf{a}$ and $\mathbf{x}$ in the space. Note that $(\mathbf{Q}\mathbf{a})^T \mathbf{Q}\mathbf{x} =$

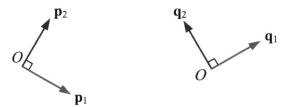

(a) Orthogonal Row Vectors (b) Orthogonal Column Vectors
Figure 28. Orthogonal Matrix. (a) The row vectors of an orthogonal matrix, like the one shown in (43), stand at perfect right angles to each other and have the same unit length. (b) And guess what? The column vectors do the same cool trick!

$\mathbf{a}^T \underline{\mathbf{Q}^T \mathbf{Q}} \mathbf{x}$. Think of $\mathbf{Q} := [\mathbf{q}_1 \, \mathbf{q}_2 \, \cdots \, \mathbf{q}_n]$ as a dream team of super players. They're not only perpendicular to each other, but they all also have a unit length, as shown in Figure 28:

$$\mathbf{q}_i^T \mathbf{q}_j = \begin{cases} 1 \text{ if } i = j \\ 0 \text{ if } i \neq j. \end{cases} \tag{41}$$

Beyond its algebraic simplicity, the orthogonal transformation is also quite visually intuitive.

The orthogonal transformation is truly fascinating! The best part is that its forward actions are much simpler than complex linear mapping. First, its analytical action is like a magical move that can rotate or flip a vector right in the same space (see Figure 29a). It's as if it's swinging a vector around, like pendulum! Then, its synthetic action is like weighted sum of the column vectors of $\mathbf{Q}$ with $\mathbf{x}$ (look at Figure 29b):

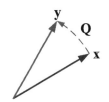
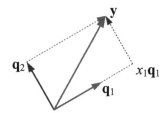

(a) Forward Rotation   (b) Orthogonal Combination

Figure 29. Orthogonal Transformation. (a) An orthogonal transformation rotates a vector. (b) It is equivalent to a linear combination of orthogonal column vectors.

$$\mathbf{Qx} = x_1\mathbf{q}_1 + x_2\mathbf{q}_2 + \cdots + x_n\mathbf{q}_n. \tag{42}$$

Think of it as creating a special blend of independent things. In fact, it is a special case of the Parallelogram Law with a rectangle thanks to the orthogonal vectors. That's why we call it an *orthogonal combination* or *orthogonal composition*.

Let's see the magic of an orthogonal transformation in action! Take, for example, a matrix that rotates a point by 30 degrees on the coordinate plane:

$$\mathbf{Q} = \frac{1}{2}\begin{bmatrix} \sqrt{3} & -1 \\ 1 & \sqrt{3} \end{bmatrix}. \tag{43}$$

When we apply this matrix, $\mathbf{Q}$, to a point like $\mathbf{x} = (\sqrt{3}, 1)$, it magically turns $\mathbf{x}$ into $\mathbf{y} = (1, \sqrt{3})$ (as seen in Figure 29a):

$$\mathbf{y} = \mathbf{Qx} \tag{44}$$

$$= \left(\frac{1}{2} \begin{bmatrix} \sqrt{3} & -1 \\ 1 & \sqrt{3} \end{bmatrix} \right) \begin{bmatrix} \sqrt{3} \\ 1 \end{bmatrix}$$

$$= \begin{bmatrix} 1 \\ \sqrt{3} \end{bmatrix}.$$

You can think of its synthetic action as an orthogonal combination of the unit vectors with $\mathbf{x} = (\sqrt{3}, 1)$ (see Figure 29b):

$$\mathbf{x}' = x_1 \mathbf{q}_1 + x_2 \mathbf{q}_2$$

$$= \sqrt{3} \left(\frac{1}{2} \begin{bmatrix} \sqrt{3} \\ 1 \end{bmatrix} \right) + \left(\frac{1}{2} \begin{bmatrix} -1 \\ \sqrt{3} \end{bmatrix} \right) \qquad (45)$$

$$= \begin{bmatrix} 1 \\ \sqrt{3} \end{bmatrix}.$$

And there you have it! That's how the orthogonal transformation does its magic in the synthetic action.

The true power of the orthogonal transformation is unveiled when we take its inverse simply by the transpose of its orthogonal matrix. This is where the magic happens! The inverse of the orthogonal matrix also rotates or flips a vector right in the same vector space, but in the opposite direction (see Figure 30a). Alternatively, the transpose of the orthogonal matrix dissects a vector using its column vectors and gather them into another vector (see Figure 30b). The inner products of column vectors with a vector $\mathbf{y}$ are as follows:

$$\mathbf{x} = \mathbf{Q}^T \mathbf{y}$$

$$\lceil \mathbf{q}_1^T \mathbf{x} \rceil \qquad (46)$$

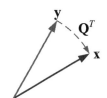
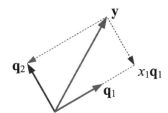

(a) Backward Rotation   (b) Orthogonal Decomposition

Figure 30. Transpose of Orthogonal Matrix. (a) As an orthogonal transformation rotates a vector, the transpose of its orthogonal matrix rotates a vector oppositely. (b) It is equivalent to orthogonal decomposition.

$$= \begin{bmatrix} \mathbf{q}_2^T \mathbf{x} \\ \vdots \\ \mathbf{q}_n^T \mathbf{x} \end{bmatrix}.$$

Each of these components $\mathbf{q}_i^T \mathbf{y}$ captures a directional part of $\mathbf{y}$ along the unit vector $\mathbf{q}_i$. It's like looking at $\mathbf{y}$ from different angles through $\mathbf{Q} := [\mathbf{q}_1 \ \mathbf{q}_2 \ \cdots \ \mathbf{q}_n]$'s eyes, revealing its unique characteristics. For the same example of (43), $\mathbf{Q}^T$ rotates a point like $\mathbf{y} = (1, \sqrt{3})$ by 30 degrees in the opposite direction on the coordinate plane (see Figure 30a):

$$\mathbf{x} = \mathbf{Q}^T \mathbf{y}$$

$$= \left(\frac{1}{2} \begin{bmatrix} \sqrt{3} & 1 \\ -1 & \sqrt{3} \end{bmatrix} \right) \begin{bmatrix} 1 \\ \sqrt{3} \end{bmatrix} \tag{47}$$

$$= \begin{bmatrix} \sqrt{3} \\ 1 \end{bmatrix}.$$

Or, you can view this as an orthogonal decomposition of $\mathbf{y} = (1, \sqrt{3})$ using the orthogonal unit vectors (Figure 30b):

$$\mathbf{x} = \begin{bmatrix} \mathbf{q}_1^T \mathbf{y} \\ \mathbf{q}_2^T \mathbf{y} \end{bmatrix}$$

$$= \begin{bmatrix} \left(\frac{1}{2}[\sqrt{3} \ \ 1]\begin{bmatrix} 1 \\ \sqrt{3} \end{bmatrix}\right) \\ \left(\frac{1}{2}[-1 \ \sqrt{3}]\begin{bmatrix} 1 \\ \sqrt{3} \end{bmatrix}\right) \end{bmatrix} \quad (48)$$

$$= \begin{bmatrix} \sqrt{3} \\ 1 \end{bmatrix}.$$

This illustrates the analytic action of the orthogonal mapping.

So, let's sum it all up. The orthogonal transformation is pretty magical! It's all thanks to its orthogonal matrix, which has the simple inverse by transpose and offers fantastic orthogonal composition and decomposition:

(a) Orthogonal Combination: This is a linear combination of its orthogonal column vectors with a vector.

(b) Orthogonal Decomposition: This is collecting inner products of its orthogonal row vectors with the vector.

You can choose which tool to use depending on whether you want to compose something new or inspect a vector closely. It's like having a magic wand with different spells to cast!

The orthogonal mappings can compose a linear mapping. The diagonal mapping handles many linear functions in an Eigen heaven. The orthogonal transformation is like a magical portal that moves a vector back and forth to the Eigen heaven. So, to put it all together, we can pair up special orthogonal vectors to compose the linear mapping.

2.4. Biorthogonal Mappings

Biorthogonal mappings form a linear mapping, offering us a way to grasp its complete picture. A matrix, on its own, lacks the broader insight of its linear mapping. The only part that's computationally easy is its forward action, much like matrix-vector multiplication. However, visualizing the entire picture of the linear mapping can be challenging. In fact, understanding where a point goes is hard, even for a two-by-two matrix, as below, until its value is actually calculated (see Figure 11):

$$A = \begin{bmatrix} 1.0 & 0.5 \\ 0.2 & 1.1 \end{bmatrix}. \tag{49}$$

A couple of methods break down a matrix into two pieces and show some aspects of its linear mapping (see Figure 31). For

a) LU Decomposition   (b) QR Decomposition

Figure 31. Matrix Decompositions. (a) Lower and upper triangular matrices represent a matrix. (b) An orthogonal and triangular matrices also form a matrix.

instance, LU decomposition factorizes a matrix into a lower triangular matrix **L** and an upper triangular matrix **U** efficiently (§3). Numerically stable, the QR decomposition factorizes a matrix into an orthogonal matrix **Q** and a right triangular matrix **R**. However, neither of these methods gives us an insight or big picture of the linear mapping.

Among all matrix decompositions, Biorthogonal Decomposition (BoD) provides unified and visual intuitions of its forward and backward actions. BoD breaks down a matrix **A** $\in \mathbb{R}^{m \times n}$ into diagonal and orthogonal matrices (Figure 32):

$$\mathbf{A} = \mathbf{V\Sigma U}^T, \tag{50}$$

where $\mathbf{U} := [\mathbf{u}_1 \ \mathbf{u}_2 \ \cdots \ \mathbf{u}_n]$ and $\mathbf{V} := [\mathbf{v}_1 \ \mathbf{v}_2 \ \cdots \ \mathbf{v}_m]$ are orthogo-

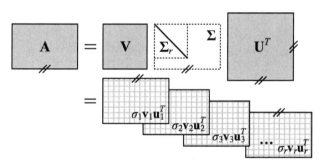

Figure 32. Biorthogonal Decomposition. A rectangular matrix is decomposed by an orthogonal matrix on the left, diagonal matrix in the middle, and another orthogonal matrix on the right. Equivalently, it is a weighted sum of biorthogonal matrices.

nal matrices in the domain and codomain, respectively, and Σ is a diagonal matrix of singular values:

$$\Sigma := \begin{bmatrix} \Sigma_r & 0 \\ 0 & 0 \end{bmatrix}, \tag{51}$$

where Σ_r is the leading square diagonal matrix:

$$\Sigma_r := \begin{bmatrix} \sigma_1 & & & \\ & \sigma_2 & & \\ & & \ddots & \\ & & & \sigma_r \end{bmatrix}. \tag{52}$$

with $\sigma_1, \sigma_2, \cdots, \sigma_r$ being the nonzero singular values. BoD is also known as the Singular Value Decomposition (SVD). In a sense, a matrix is a weighted sum of biorthogonal matrices:

$$A = \sum_{k=1}^{r} \sigma_k v_k u_k^T, \tag{53}$$

where $v_k u_k^T$ is the biorthogonal matrix corresponding to σ_k (Figure 32). So, a linear mapping involves three simpler steps:

$$\begin{aligned} y &= Ax \\ &= V\Sigma U^T x. \end{aligned} \tag{54}$$

For a point, the linear mapping takes its orthogonal decomposition, axis-aligned scaling, and orthogonal combination.

Magically speaking, an Eigen turn of a vector space turns it into Eigen heaven (see Figure 33a to b). In Eigen heaven, all components are individually scaled up and down (from Figure 33b to c). Another Eigen turn turns Eigen heaven back

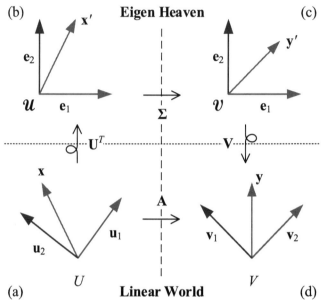

Figure 33. Forward Action of a Linear Mapping. A linear mapping might be complicated even in the linear world while its biorthogonal decomposition makes it easy via its Eigen heaven.

into another vector space (from Figure 33c to d). Given a vector **x**, decompose the vector **x** into the Eigen basis of the domain, scale the individual coordinates of the decomposed one **x'**, and compose another vector **y** corresponding to the scaled coordinates **y'** on another Eigen basis of the codomain.

Consider a simple example of the two-by-two matrix **A** in (49) that maps $\mathbf{x} = (-0.5, 1.0)$ to $\mathbf{y} = (0.0, 1.0)$:

$$\mathbf{y} = \mathbf{A}\mathbf{x}$$

$$= \begin{bmatrix} 1.0 & 0.5 \\ 0.2 & 1.1 \end{bmatrix} \begin{bmatrix} -0.5 \\ 1.0 \end{bmatrix}$$

$$= \begin{bmatrix} 0.0 \\ 1.0 \end{bmatrix}. \tag{55}$$

Matrix multiplication alone doesn't offer much insight into the linear mapping. Let's explore the biorthogonal mapping step by step with this example. The BoD of the matrix $\mathbf{A}$ is:

$$\mathbf{A} = \left(\frac{1}{\sqrt{2}} \begin{bmatrix} 1 & -1 \\ 1 & 1 \end{bmatrix} \right) \left(\frac{1}{\sqrt{2}} \begin{bmatrix} 2 & 0 \\ 0 & 1 \end{bmatrix} \right) \left(\frac{1}{5} \begin{bmatrix} 3 & 4 \\ -4 & 3 \end{bmatrix} \right). \tag{56}$$

Three orthogonal mappings demonstrate how the forward action of the linear mapping works. First, $\mathbf{x}$ is projected onto column eigenvectors and enters Eigen heaven (Figure 33b):

$$\mathbf{x}' = \mathbf{U}^T \mathbf{x}$$

$$= \left(\frac{1}{5} \begin{bmatrix} 3 & 4 \\ -4 & 3 \end{bmatrix} \right) \begin{bmatrix} -0.5 \\ 1.0 \end{bmatrix} \tag{57}$$

$$= \begin{bmatrix} 0.5 \\ 1.0 \end{bmatrix}.$$

Next, each elements of $\mathbf{x}'$ in the Eigen heaven is scaled by the corresponding diagonal element of $\mathbf{\Sigma}$ to $\mathbf{y}'$ (Figure 33c):

$$\mathbf{y}' = \mathbf{\Sigma} \mathbf{x}'$$

$$= \left(\frac{1}{\sqrt{2}} \begin{bmatrix} 2 & 0 \\ 0 & 1 \end{bmatrix} \right) \begin{bmatrix} 0.5 \\ 1.0 \end{bmatrix} \tag{58}$$

$$= \frac{1}{\sqrt{2}} \begin{bmatrix} 1.0 \\ 1.0 \end{bmatrix}.$$

Finally, we compose $\mathbf{y}$ by combining $\mathbf{V}$ with $\mathbf{y}'$ (Figure 33d):

$$\mathbf{y} = \mathbf{V}\mathbf{y}'$$

$$= \left(\frac{1}{\sqrt{2}} \begin{bmatrix} 1 & -1 \\ 1 & 1 \end{bmatrix} \right) \left(\frac{1}{\sqrt{2}} \begin{bmatrix} 1.0 \\ 1.0 \end{bmatrix} \right) \tag{59}$$

$$= \begin{bmatrix} 0.0 \\ 1.0 \end{bmatrix}.$$

This step-by-step process helps us understand how the biorthogonal mapping works and directs points within the space.

A direct action of the linear mapping from the domain to the codomain is possible with biorthogonal bases (see Figure 34). The identity mapping between paired orthogonal bases of the domain and codomin is straightforward. Combine the second scaling step and third composing step:

$$\mathbf{V}' := \mathbf{V}\mathbf{\Sigma} \tag{60}$$

$$= [\mathbf{v}_1' \ \mathbf{v}_2' \ \cdots \ \mathbf{v}_n']$$

where $\mathbf{v}_i'$ is the i-th scaled vector (Figure 34d):

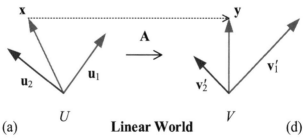

Figure 34. Biorthogonal Action of a Linear Mapping. Combining the second and third orthogonal steps, a direct mapping from the domain to the codomain with orthogonal bases is intuitive.

$$\mathbf{v}_i' := \begin{cases} \sigma_i \mathbf{v}_i & \text{for } i = 1,2,\cdots,r \\ \mathbf{0} & \text{otherwise.} \end{cases} \tag{61}$$

$\mathbf{A}$ is written by paired orthogonal matrices:

$$\mathbf{A} = \mathbf{V}'\mathbf{U}^T. \tag{62}$$

In essence, the biorthogonal action of a linear mapping preserves the coordinates of two corresponding points in their orthogonal bases. With the same matrix above in (56),

$$\mathbf{A} = \left(\frac{1}{2}\begin{bmatrix} 2 & -1 \\ 2 & 1 \end{bmatrix}\right)\left(\frac{1}{5}\begin{bmatrix} 3 & 4 \\ -4 & 3 \end{bmatrix}\right). \tag{63}$$

As half of $\mathbf{u}_1$ and one $\mathbf{u}_2$ compose $\mathbf{x} = (-0.5, 1.0)$ in the domain, half of $\mathbf{v}_1'$ and one $\mathbf{v}_2'$ do $\mathbf{y} = (0.0, 1.0)$ in the range.

A singular linear mapping with zero singular values attracts particular interest (Figure 35). The singular linear mapping maps many vectors in the domain maps to a vector in the codomain. Suppose the second singular value is zero, that is, $\sigma_2 = 0$. If the linear mapping maps $\mathbf{x}$ to $\mathbf{y}$ in the range,

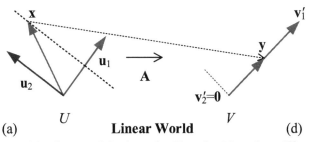

(a) U **Linear World** V (d)

Figure 35. Biorthogonal Action of a Singular Mapping. All points on the dotted line in U are mapped to a point in V.

it also maps the other vectors on the line passing through $\mathbf{x}$ and in parallel with $\mathbf{u}_2$ to $\mathbf{y}$ (Figure 35a). This is because any coordinate for $\mathbf{u}_2$ in the domain vanishes to zero in the corresponding coordinate in the codomain, regardless of its value. For example, consider a two-by-two square matrix:

$$\mathbf{A} = \begin{bmatrix} 0.6 & 0.8 \\ 0.6 & 0.8 \end{bmatrix}. \tag{64}$$

The constant ratios rowwise and columnwise hint at the matrix having a zero singular value, implying the dependency of the row and column vectors. Its singularity is obvious with its Biorthogonal Decomposition (BoD):

$$\mathbf{A} = \left(\frac{1}{\sqrt{2}} \begin{bmatrix} 1 & -1 \\ 1 & 1 \end{bmatrix} \right) \left(\frac{1}{\sqrt{2}} \begin{bmatrix} 2 & 0 \\ 0 & 0 \end{bmatrix} \right) \left(\frac{1}{5} \begin{bmatrix} 3 & 4 \\ -4 & 3 \end{bmatrix} \right). \tag{65}$$

Note that the second singular value is zero. Corresponding to the zero singular value, its scaled vector of biorthogonal basis

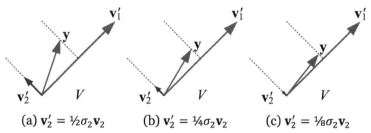

(a) $\mathbf{v}_2' = \tfrac{1}{2}\sigma_2 \mathbf{v}_2$ (b) $\mathbf{v}_2' = \tfrac{1}{4}\sigma_2 \mathbf{v}_2$ (c) $\mathbf{v}_2' = \tfrac{1}{8}\sigma_2 \mathbf{v}_2$

Figure 36. Vanishing Singular Value. As the first singular value vanishes from Figure 34d to 35d, its dyadic steps animates how it squashes everything along its eigenvector in the codomain.

vanishes to zero. It inroduces the null space in the domain and the left null space in the codomain along the vectors corresponding to the zero singular value. As a singular value vanishes to zero, intermediate steps animate how it squashes everything along its eigenvector in the codomain (Figure 36).

The biorthogonal decomposition of a linear mapping reveals its forward action using a split-solve-merge technique: breaking down an input vector into individual components, addressing them one by one, and then combining their results into the output vector. The first dividing step involves analyzing the input vector. The second conquering step is a straightforward multiplication process. The third step combines the intermediate results to produce the final output.

The four fundamental subspaces outline a big picture of a linear mapping: row space, column space, null space, and left null space (see Figure 37). Note that the range of a linear mapping T specified by a matrix $\mathbf{A}$, that is, $T(\mathbf{x}) = \mathbf{Ax}$, consists of all linear combinations of $\mathbf{A}$'s column vectors:

$$\begin{aligned}\mathcal{R}(\mathbf{A}) &:= \mathcal{R}(T) \\ &= \{\mathbf{Ax} | \mathbf{x} \in \mathcal{D}(\mathbf{A})\}.\end{aligned} \tag{66}$$

$\mathcal{R}(\mathbf{A})$ is a subspace of the codomain $\mathbb{R}^m$ called *column space*. There is another subspace of the domain $\mathbb{R}^n$ called *null space* of T, where $\mathbf{A}$ nullifies all vectors into the zero vector:

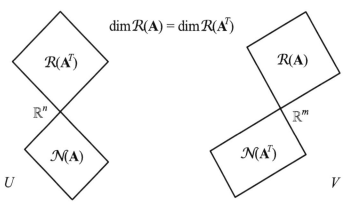

Figure 37. The Four Fundamental Subspaces. The four fundamental spaces cubistically span the domain and codomain [2].
The row and null spaces span the domain on the left. The column and left null spaces span the codomain on the right.

$$\mathcal{N}(\mathbf{A}) := \{\mathbf{x} \in \mathcal{D}(\mathbf{A}) | \mathbf{A}\mathbf{x} = \mathbf{0}\}. \tag{67}$$

$\mathbf{A}^T$ induces a fascinating twist of a linear mapping, switching
$\mathbf{A}$'s domain and codomain. The range of $\mathbf{A}^T$, $\mathcal{R}(\mathbf{A}^T)$, or *row
space* of $\mathbf{A}$ is a subspace of the domain $\mathbb{R}^n$, while the null
space of $\mathbf{A}^T$, $\mathcal{N}(\mathbf{A}^T)$, or the *left null space* of $\mathbf{A}$ is a subspace
of the codomain $\mathbb{R}^m$. Together, these four fundamental sub-
spaces artistically span the domain and codomain.

In contrast, Biorthogonal Decomposition of a linear mapping vividly illustrates its fundamental subspaces in space
(see Figure 38). Focus only on the identity mapping in the
Eigen heaven, to which composition and decomposition with

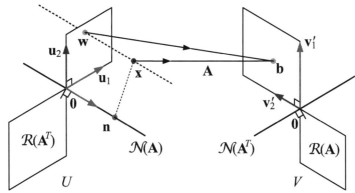

Figure 38. Fundamental Subspaces. Two-dimensional row and column spaces and one-dimensional null spaces are visible in three-dimensional linear world. Biorthogonal bases of row and column spaces have one-to-one correspondences.

orthogonal bases pair up to shuttle a vector back and forth from the vector spaces. Consider a vivid example in a three-dimensional space with a three-by-three matrix:

$$A = \begin{bmatrix} 0.48 & 0.12 & 0.36 \\ 0.40 & 1.10 & 0.30 \\ 0.64 & 0.16 & 0.48 \end{bmatrix} \tag{68}$$

of which Biorthogonal Decomposition is

$$A = \left(\frac{1}{25}\begin{bmatrix} 9 & -12 & -20 \\ 20 & 15 & 0 \\ 12 & -16 & 15 \end{bmatrix}\right)\left(\frac{1}{\sqrt{2}}\begin{bmatrix} 2 & 0 & 0 \\ 0 & 1 & 0 \\ 0 & 0 & 0 \end{bmatrix}\right)\left(\frac{1}{5\sqrt{2}}\begin{bmatrix} 4 & 5 & 3 \\ -4 & 5 & -3 \\ 3\sqrt{2} & 0 & 4\sqrt{2} \end{bmatrix}\right).$$

Here, the row and column spaces exist in two-dimensional planes, while the null spaces exist in one-dimensional lines. The orthogonal bases pair up one by one on row and column spaces, ensuring that corresponding points pre-serve their coordinates in their orthogonal bases. As depicted in Figure 34, the invertible linear mapping between row and column spaces is embedded as subspaces in Figure 38. The linear mapping basically teleports the same coordinates from its domain to the codomain with their orthogonal bases.

Fantastic job in grasping the big picture of linear mappings! By understanding the Biorthogonal Decomposition of a linear mapping, you've unlocked a fresh perspective on the domain and codomain, including the fundamental subspaces. This conceptual leap empowers you to comprehend the intricate relationships between various subspaces, offering valuable insights into the behavior of linear mappings. Keep up the fantastic work, and relish delving into the exciting world of linear mappings! Embrace the beauty of this linear world, and find joy in the captivating exploration that lies ahead!

The fundamenatal subspaces come with important properties. The column and row spaces share the same dimension:

$$\dim \mathcal{R}(\mathbf{A}) = \dim \mathcal{R}(\mathbf{A}^T), \tag{69}$$

where $\dim S$ is the dimension of a subspace S. To prove this, suppose all column vectors of $\mathbf{A} \in \mathbb{R}^{m \times n}$ are linear combinations of a basis with $r := \dim \mathcal{R}(\mathbf{A})$ independent vectors:

$$\mathbf{A} = \mathbf{BC}, \tag{70}$$

where $\mathbf{B} := [\mathbf{b}_1 \; \mathbf{b}_2 \; \cdots \; \mathbf{b}_r] \in \mathbb{R}^{m \times r}$ is the basis matrix and $\mathbf{C} \in \mathbb{R}^{r \times n}$ is the composition matrix of the linear combinations. In a sense, $\mathbf{A}$'s row vectors are linear combinations of $\mathbf{C}$'s row vectors. So, the dimension of the row space is at most r:

$$\dim \mathcal{R}(\mathbf{A}^T) \leq \dim \mathcal{R}(\mathbf{A}). \tag{71}$$

Applying the same argument to $\mathbf{A}^T$, we find:

$$\dim \mathcal{R}(\mathbf{A}) \leq \dim \mathcal{R}(\mathbf{A}^T). \tag{72}$$

Hence, the row and column spaces have the same dimension, which equals the number of nonzero singular values (52).

For a linear mapping, its fundamental subspaces provide a clear picture of its input and output spaces (Figure 38). The input space splits into two orthogonal subspaces: the row and null spaces. Similarly, the output space splits into two orthogonal subspaces: the column and left null spaces. The row and null spaces are orthogonal as so are their elements in the input space. To prove this, suppose an arbitrary null vector $\mathbf{n}$ in $\mathcal{N}(\mathbf{A})$, meaning $\mathbf{An} = \mathbf{0}$. For any vector $\mathbf{w}$ in the row space, there exists a vector $\mathbf{y}$ in the output space such that $\mathbf{A}^T\mathbf{y} = \mathbf{w}$. Then, $\mathbf{n}$ and $\mathbf{w}$ are orthogonal (Figure 38):

$$\mathbf{w}^T\mathbf{n} = (\mathbf{A}^T\mathbf{y})^T\mathbf{n} = \mathbf{y}^T\mathbf{An} = 0. \tag{73}$$

Similarly, the column and left null spaces are orthogonal in the output space.

3. Linear Systems

Imagine a bunch of linear equations called a *'linear system.'* Solving a linear system sounds tricky, but it's like having a clear road map to solve general problems. Solving these math puzzles means figuring out how things link up — both going forward and backward. One way might be easy, but the other can be a bit tougher. Sketching out all connections seem a bit boring and hard to get the whole picture. However, the linear system has a special trick that makes it simpler to see how it moves forward and backward using orthogonal mappings.

Just like a linear equation, a linear system also has three kinds of solutions (compare Tables 2 and 5). Solving a linear system involves working backward from its forward mapping:

$$\mathbf{Ax} = \mathbf{b}, \qquad (74)$$

where $\mathbf{A}$ is a coefficient matrix, $\mathbf{x}$ is an unknown vector in the input space, and $\mathbf{b}$ is a constant vector in the output space.

Table 5. Types of Linear Systems. The column and null spaces characterize the three types of the linear system.

$\mathcal{N}(\mathbf{A})$ \ $\mathcal{R}(\mathbf{A})$	$\mathbf{b} \in \mathcal{R}(\mathbf{A})$	$\mathbf{b} \notin \mathcal{R}(\mathbf{A})$
$\mathcal{N}(\mathbf{A}) = \{\mathbf{0}\}$	Unique Solution (§3.2)	No Solution (§3.4)
$\mathcal{N}(\mathbf{A}) \neq \{\mathbf{0}\}$	Many Solutions (§3.3)	

Its solution set is the collection of all solutions:

$$S(\mathbf{A}, \mathbf{b}) := \{\mathbf{x} \in \mathcal{D}(\mathbf{A}) | \mathbf{A}\mathbf{x} = \mathbf{b}\}. \tag{75}$$

If the constant vector of the linear system fits in the range of its linear mapping, then it has a solution. Otherwise, it has no solution. A determined system has a unique solution, an underdetermined system has infinitely many solutions, and an overdetermined system has no solution.

In order to solve a linear system, one popular method is Gauss elimination or row reduction. This method reduces the number of variables incrementally to one and solves the elementary linear equations backwardly in a row. For example,

$$\begin{aligned} x + 2y &= 3 \\ 3x + 5y &= 4. \end{aligned} \tag{76}$$

By eliminating x in the second equation with the first, we get:

$$\begin{aligned} x + 2y &= 3 \\ y &= 5. \end{aligned} \tag{77}$$

Substituting $y = 5$, we find $x = -7$ from the first equation. So, the Gauss elimination helps solve variables one by one until we end up with an elementary linear equation. If at any point we run into a singular case, then so is the linear system. While these steps are clear and direct, seeing the backward actions of the linear system can be a bit challenging.

3.1. Invertible System

A linear system is said *invertible* if you can uniquely reverse it back to its input. For a square matrix $\mathbf{A}$, it is *invertible* if there is another matrix $\mathbf{X}$ of the same size such that:

$$\mathbf{AX} = \mathbf{XA} = \mathbf{I}, \tag{78}$$

where $\mathbf{X}$ is the inverse of $\mathbf{A}$, written as $\mathbf{A}^{-1}$. If you multiply two square matrices $\mathbf{A}$ and $\mathbf{B}$, the inverse of their product is the product of their inverses in reverse order:

$$(\mathbf{AB})^{-1} = \mathbf{B}^{-1}\mathbf{A}^{-1}. \tag{79}$$

An invertible linear system with $\mathbf{A}$ has a unique solution for any vector $\mathbf{y}$ in the output space, found using:

$$\mathbf{x} = \mathbf{A}^{-1}\mathbf{y}. \tag{80}$$

All linear systems — *determined, underdetermined,* or *overdetermined* — embed an invertible system that connects the row and column spaces with one-to-one correspondences.

Let's talk about what happens with the invertible system using Biorthogonal Decomposition (BoD). From BoD of an invertible matrix $\mathbf{A}$ as in (50), we get BoD of $\mathbf{A}^{-1}$:

$$\begin{aligned} \mathbf{A}^{-1} &= (\mathbf{V}\boldsymbol{\Sigma}\mathbf{U}^T)^{-1} \\ &= (\mathbf{U}^T)^{-1}\boldsymbol{\Sigma}^{-1}\mathbf{V}^{-1} \\ &= \mathbf{U}\boldsymbol{\Sigma}^{-1}\mathbf{V}^T, \end{aligned} \tag{81}$$

where $(\mathbf{U}^T)^{-1} = \mathbf{U}$ and $\mathbf{V}^{-1} = \mathbf{V}^T$ because $\mathbf{U}$ and $\mathbf{V}$ are orthogonal matrices. All singular values of $\mathbf{A}$ in Σ_r are not zeros:

$$\sigma_k \neq 0 \text{ for } k = 1,2,\cdots,r, \tag{82}$$

where $r = \dim \mathcal{R}(\mathbf{A}) = \dim \mathcal{R}(\mathbf{A}^T)$. So, Σ_r^{-1} is a square diagonal matrix with reciprocals of the diagonal elements in Σ_r:

$$\Sigma_r^{-1} = \begin{bmatrix} \sigma_1^{-1} & & & \\ & \sigma_2^{-1} & & \\ & & \ddots & \\ & & & \sigma_r^{-1} \end{bmatrix}. \tag{83}$$

The inverse mapping of an invertible system results in the unique solution for any constant vector $\mathbf{b}$ in the output space:

$$\begin{aligned} \mathbf{x} &= \mathbf{A}^{-1}\mathbf{b} \\ &= \mathbf{U}\Sigma^{-1}\mathbf{V}^T\mathbf{b}. \end{aligned} \tag{84}$$

In fact, the invertible linear mapping establishes one-to-one correspondences between the input and output spaces.

Graphically, the invertible linear mapping moves back and forth between the input and output spaces through orthogonal mappings (see Figure 39). The backward action of the linear mapping takes opposite steps of its forward action. Magically speaking, an Eigen turn of a target point $\mathbf{b}$ in a linear world turns the linear world into its Eigen heaven (from Figure 39d to c), where everything is straightforward one to one (from Figure 39c to b). Another Eigen turn of the heavenly point turns the Eigen heaven back into the linear world and results in the source point $\mathbf{x}$ (from Figure 39b to a).

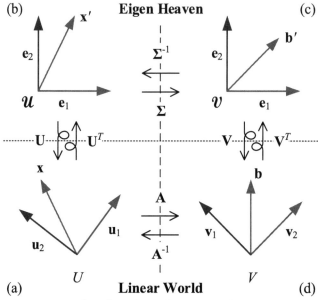

Figure 39. Forward and Backward Actions of a Linear Mapping. The biorthogonal decomposition makes the complicated backward action easy via its Eigen heaven as in Figure 33.

The backward action of a linear mapping with an invertible matrix results in the unique solution of the linear system. Three orthogonal steps from Figure 39d through c and b to a show how the backward action of the linear mapping works. Consider a linear system with the coefficient matrix **A** in (49) and constant vector **b** = (0.0, 1.0). $\mathbf{A}^{-1}$ and its BoD are

$$\mathbf{A}^{-1} = \begin{bmatrix} 1.1 & -0.5 \\ -0.2 & 1.0 \end{bmatrix} \tag{85}$$

$$= \left(\frac{1}{5} \begin{bmatrix} 3 & -4 \\ 4 & 3 \end{bmatrix} \right) \left(\frac{1}{\sqrt{2}} \begin{bmatrix} 1 & 0 \\ 0 & 2 \end{bmatrix} \right) \left(\frac{1}{\sqrt{2}} \begin{bmatrix} 1 & 1 \\ -1 & 1 \end{bmatrix} \right).$$

First, **V** decomposes **b** into **b′** (from Figure 39d to c):

$$\mathbf{b}' = \mathbf{V}^T \mathbf{b}$$

$$= \left(\frac{1}{\sqrt{2}} \begin{bmatrix} 1 & 1 \\ -1 & 1 \end{bmatrix} \right) \begin{bmatrix} 0.0 \\ 1.0 \end{bmatrix} \tag{86}$$

$$= \frac{1}{\sqrt{2}} \begin{bmatrix} 1.0 \\ 1.0 \end{bmatrix}.$$

Then **b′** is inversely scaled by $\mathbf{\Sigma}^{-1}$ to **x′** (from Figure 39c to b):

$$\mathbf{x}' = \mathbf{\Sigma}^{-1} \mathbf{b}'$$

$$= \left(\frac{1}{\sqrt{2}} \begin{bmatrix} 1 & 0 \\ 0 & 2 \end{bmatrix} \right) \left(\frac{1}{\sqrt{2}} \begin{bmatrix} 1.0 \\ 1.0 \end{bmatrix} \right) \tag{87}$$

$$= \begin{bmatrix} 0.5 \\ 1.0 \end{bmatrix}.$$

Finally, we can compose **x** out of **x′** (from Figure 39b to a):

$$\mathbf{x} = \mathbf{U}\mathbf{x}'$$

$$= \left(\frac{1}{5} \begin{bmatrix} 3 & -4 \\ 4 & 3 \end{bmatrix} \right) \begin{bmatrix} 0.5 \\ 1.0 \end{bmatrix} \tag{88}$$

$$= \begin{bmatrix} -0.5 \\ 1.0 \end{bmatrix}.$$

Thus $\mathbf{x} = (-0.5, 1.0)$ is the solution out of $\mathbf{b} = (0.0, 1.0)$.

Direct action of the inverse mapping from its input space to output space is possible with orthogonal bases (Figure 40). Combine the first decomposing step ($\mathbf{V}^T$) and second scaling step ($\mathbf{\Sigma}^{-1}$) and we have paired orthogonal matrices for $\mathbf{A}^{-1}$:

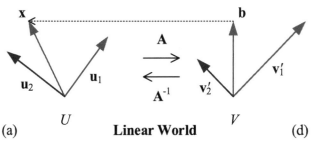

(a) U **Linear World** V (d)

Figure 40. Biorthogonal Action of an Inverse Mapping. Combining the first and second orthogonal steps, a direct mapping from the codomain to the domain with orthogonal bases is intuitive.

$$\mathbf{A}^{-1} = \mathbf{U}(\mathbf{V}')^{-1}, \tag{89}$$

where $(\mathbf{V}')^{-1} = \mathbf{\Sigma}^{-1}\mathbf{V}^T$. With the same example above,

$$\mathbf{A} = \left(\frac{1}{5}\begin{bmatrix} 3 & -4 \\ 4 & 3 \end{bmatrix}\right)\left(\frac{1}{2}\begin{bmatrix} 2 & 2 \\ -1 & 1 \end{bmatrix}\right). \tag{90}$$

Then, half $\mathbf{u}_1$ and $\mathbf{u}_2$ result in $\mathbf{x} = (-0.5, 1.0)$ as half $\mathbf{v}'_1$ and $\mathbf{v}'_2$ compose $\mathbf{b} = (0.0, 1.0)$. Basically, the coordinates of an output vector in the codomain's Eigen basis compose the input vector in the domain's Eigen basis.

3.2. Determined System

A linear system is *determined* if it has the same number of independent equations and unknown variables. It has enough clues to solve a mystery — it means we can find one and only one solution. In the big picture of a linear mapping, a

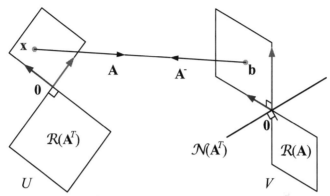

Figure 41. Determined System. A determined system has the trivial null space and a constant vector in the column space.

determined system has the trivial null space (Figure 41):

$$\mathcal{N}(\mathbf{A}) = \{\mathbf{0}\}. \tag{91}$$

So, the coefficient matrix $\mathbf{A}$ has nonzero singular values:

$$\mathbf{A} = \mathbf{V}\begin{bmatrix} \boldsymbol{\Sigma}_r \\ \mathbf{0} \end{bmatrix}\mathbf{U}^T. \tag{92}$$

The determined system results in the unique solution only when a constant vector is in the range or column space:

$$\mathbf{b} \in \mathcal{R}(\mathbf{A}). \tag{93}$$

Otherwise, the linear system has no solution (see §3.4).

There's something called a generalized inverse to find the unique solution for a determined system. BoD of a coefficient matrix is the same as that of the invertible system except a little tweak for the inverse diagonal mapping (see §4.2 for full

derivation). For a coefficient matrix $\mathbf{A}$ of a determined system, its generalized inverse $\mathbf{A}^-$ looks like this:

$$\mathbf{A}^- := \mathbf{U}\boldsymbol{\Sigma}^-\mathbf{V}^T, \tag{94}$$

where $\boldsymbol{\Sigma}^-$ is the generalized inverse of $\boldsymbol{\Sigma}$:

$$\boldsymbol{\Sigma}^- = [\boldsymbol{\Sigma}_r^{-1}\ \mathbf{0}]. \tag{95}$$

For example, consider a determined system of a three-by-
two matrix with simple decimal numbers (Figure 41):

$$\mathbf{A} = \begin{bmatrix} 0.8 & 0.4 \\ 0.2 & 1.1 \\ 0.6 & 0.3 \end{bmatrix}. \tag{96}$$

BoD of $\mathbf{A}$ shows its orthogonal structure:

$$\mathbf{A} = \left(\frac{1}{5\sqrt{2}} \begin{bmatrix} 4 & -4 & 3\sqrt{2} \\ 5 & 5 & 0 \\ 3 & -3 & 4\sqrt{2} \end{bmatrix} \right) \left(\frac{1}{\sqrt{2}} \begin{bmatrix} 2 & 0 \\ 0 & 1 \\ 0 & 0 \end{bmatrix} \right) \left(\frac{1}{5} \begin{bmatrix} 3 & 4 \\ -4 & 3 \end{bmatrix} \right).$$

The first magic turn turns a linear world into the Eigen hea-
ven, giving us $\mathbf{b}'$ for $\mathbf{b} = (0.0, 1.0. 0.0)$ (from Figure 39d to c):

$$\mathbf{b}' = \mathbf{V}^T\mathbf{b}$$

$$= \left(\frac{1}{5\sqrt{2}} \begin{bmatrix} 4 & 5 & 3 \\ -4 & 5 & -3 \\ 3\sqrt{2} & 0 & 4\sqrt{2} \end{bmatrix} \right) \begin{bmatrix} 0.0 \\ 1.0 \\ 0.0 \end{bmatrix} \tag{97}$$

$$= \left(\frac{1}{\sqrt{2}} \begin{bmatrix} 1.0 \\ 1.0 \\ 0.0 \end{bmatrix} \right).$$

Then $\mathbf{b}'$ is inversely scaled by $\boldsymbol{\Sigma}$ to $\mathbf{x}'$ (from Figure 39c to b):

$$\mathbf{x}' = \boldsymbol{\Sigma}^-\mathbf{b}' \tag{98}$$

$$= \left(\frac{1}{\sqrt{2}} \begin{bmatrix} 1 & 0 & 0 \\ 0 & 2 & 0 \end{bmatrix} \right) \left(\frac{1}{\sqrt{2}} \begin{bmatrix} 1.0 \\ 1.0 \\ 0.0 \end{bmatrix} \right)$$

$$= \begin{bmatrix} 0.5 \\ 1.0 \end{bmatrix}.$$

Finally, we can compose $\mathbf{x}$ out of $\mathbf{x}'$ (from Figure 39b to a):

$$\mathbf{x} = \mathbf{U}\mathbf{x}'$$

$$= \left(\frac{1}{5} \begin{bmatrix} 3 & -4 \\ 4 & 3 \end{bmatrix} \right) \begin{bmatrix} 0.5 \\ 1.0 \end{bmatrix} \qquad (99)$$

$$= \begin{bmatrix} -0.5 \\ 1.0 \end{bmatrix}.$$

$\mathbf{x} = (-0.5, 1.0)$ is the solution of the determined system for a constant vector $\mathbf{b} = (0.0, 1.0, 0.0)$ in the column space.

3.3. Underdetermined System

A linear system is termed *underdetermined* if it has fewer independent equations than unknown variables. So, the independent equations cannot exclusively determine all variables. In such systems, multiple solutions are mapped to the same point within the range. They exhibit a nontrivial null space within their input space. The solution set of an underdetermined system is the shifted null space by a specific solution:

$$S(\mathbf{A}, \mathbf{b}) = \{\mathbf{x}_p + \mathbf{x}_0 | \mathbf{A}\mathbf{x}_p = \mathbf{b}, \mathbf{x}_0 \in \mathcal{N}(\mathbf{A})\}, \qquad (100)$$

where $\mathbf{x}_p$ is the particular solution such that $\mathbf{A}\mathbf{x}_p = \mathbf{b}$. Thus the nonempty solution set is as big as the null space.

When we deal with a fat matrix in a linear system, it's underdetermined all the time. For instance, consider a simple underdetermined system with a one-by-two matrix like:

$$\mathbf{A} = [1.2 \quad 1.6]$$

$$= [1][1 \quad 0]\left(\frac{1}{5}\begin{bmatrix} 3 & 4 \\ -4 & 3 \end{bmatrix}\right). \tag{101}$$

This linear mapping maps all points in the direction of $\mathbf{u}_2$ from $0.5\mathbf{u}_1$ to the same point $0.5\mathbf{v}_1$ (see Figure 42). In reverse, the solutions for the underdetermined system with $0.5\mathbf{v}_1$ are

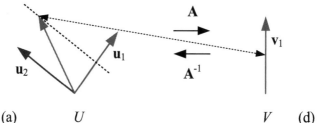

(a) U V (d)

Figure 42. Underdetermined System. All points along the direction of $\mathbf{u}_2$ from $0.5\mathbf{u}_1$ are mapped to the same point $0.5\mathbf{v}_1$.

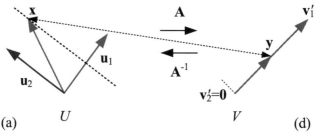

(a) U V (d)

Figure 43. Underdetermined System. All points along the direction of $\mathbf{u}_2$ from $0.5\mathbf{u}_1$ are mapped to the same point $0.5\mathbf{v}_1'$.

all points on the line parallel to $\mathbf{u}_2$ and passing through $0.5\mathbf{u}_1$:

$$\mathbf{x} = 0.5\mathbf{u}_1 + t\mathbf{u}_2, \tag{102}$$

where t is an arbitrary real number. A linear system with a square or tall skinny matrix can be underdetermined. The matrix in (64) is a good example on paper (Figure 43).

Let's consider another visible example in space using a two-by-three matrix (Figure 44). The matrix $\mathbf{A}$ looks like this:

$$\mathbf{A} = \begin{bmatrix} 0.8 & 0.2 & 0.6 \\ 0.4 & 1.1 & 0.3 \end{bmatrix}$$

$$= \left(\frac{1}{5}\begin{bmatrix} 3 & -4 \\ 4 & 3 \end{bmatrix}\right)\left(\frac{1}{\sqrt{2}}\begin{bmatrix} 2 & 0 & 0 \\ 0 & 1 & 0 \end{bmatrix}\right)\left(\frac{1}{5\sqrt{2}}\begin{bmatrix} 4 & 5 & 3 \\ -4 & 5 & -3 \\ 3\sqrt{2} & 0 & 4\sqrt{2} \end{bmatrix}\right).$$

Not only a particular solution but also all points passing through it in parallel to $\mathcal{N}(\mathbf{A})$ are solutions of the linear system

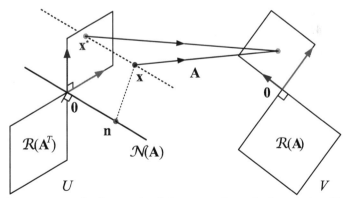

Figure 44. Underdetermined System. The solution set is a line passing through $\mathbf{x}^*$ and parallel to $\mathcal{N}(\mathbf{A})$.

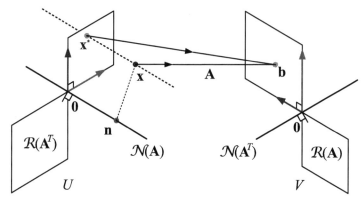

Figure 45. Augmented Underdetermined System. The solution set is a line passing through $\mathbf{x}$ and parallel to $\mathcal{N}(\mathbf{A})$.

for any constant vectors in the output space. Consider another example in the three-dimensional space in equation (68) again to illustrate a column space inside the output space, but with the third singular value being zero (Figure 45). For any constant vectors in the column space, all points passing through a particular solution in parallel to $\mathcal{N}(\mathbf{A})$ are solutions of the linear system. Indeed, both examples are underdetermined system due to their surplus unknown variables over independent equations.

3.4. Overdetermined System

Let's talk about an overdetermined system. A linear system is said *overdetermined* if it has more independent equations than unknown variables. Imagine having a bunch of rules for a problem, but these rules are too strict and don't allow you to find an answer. For an overdetermined system, think of it this way: if a constant vector lies outside the column space, the system doesn't have any element in its input space that maps to this constant vector (Figure 46). The independent equations of the overdetermined system overly constrain the variables in the linear system and prevent it from having a consistent solution uniquely.

Let's consider a small example with a two-by-one matrix:

$$\begin{bmatrix} 1 \\ 1 \end{bmatrix} \mathbf{x} = \begin{bmatrix} 0 \\ 1 \end{bmatrix}. \tag{103}$$

The Biorthogonal Decomposition of the coefficient matrix reveals that the column space forms a diagonal line passing

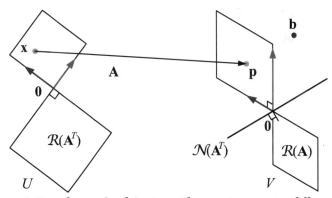

Figure 46. Overdetermined System. The constant vector falls out of the column space, that is, $\mathbf{b} \notin \mathcal{R}(\mathbf{A})$.

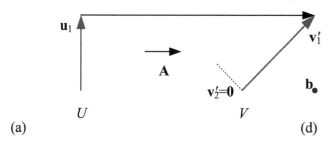

| (a) | | (d) |

Figure 47. Overdetermined System. No points are mapped to all points other than the line along the direction of $\mathbf{v}_1'$.

through the origin in the x-y plane (Figure 47d):

$$\mathbf{A} = \begin{bmatrix} 1 \\ 1 \end{bmatrix}$$

$$= \left(\frac{1}{\sqrt{2}} \begin{bmatrix} 1 & -1 \\ 1 & 1 \end{bmatrix} \right) \begin{bmatrix} \sqrt{2} \\ 0 \end{bmatrix} [1].$$

The issue here? No point in the input space maps to (1,0). It's like having two equations that are just too strict!

Let's reconsider a couple of matrices in the previous sections. Take the tall skinny matrix in equation (96) again. Its column space forms a plane passing through the origin in the three-dimensional space (see Figure 46). In this case, there are a lot points in the output space that can't be reached from any inputs. For example, there's no way to get to the point $(0,0,-1)$ no matter what inputs we try. Despite having a non-trivial null space in the input space, an overdetermined sys-

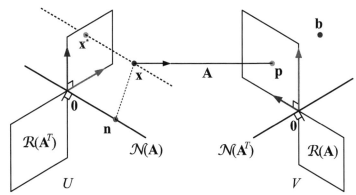

Figure 48. Augmented Overdetermined System. The constant vector falls out of the column space, that is, $\mathbf{b} \notin \mathcal{R}(\mathbf{A})$.

tem doesn't have a solution. To illustrate the four fundamental subspaces, let's examine the square matrix in equation (68) again. The input space extends to three dimensions but with the third singular value being zero (see Figure 48). All these examples showcase overdetermined systems as their constant vectors are outside the column space.

4. Quadratic Optimization†

The generalized inverse of a matrix is found by minimizing two quadratic forms using its inner and outer squares. Visually, a quadratic form is like an elliptic paraboloid (see Figure 49a). When we transform things using a matrix square, it's like reshaping vectors in a cool elliptical way (see Figure 49b). This transformation hits its lowest point at its vertex, just like finding the bottom of a valley, as its parabolic shape curves concavely in all directions (see Figure 49c). Cool, right?

Biorthogonal Decomposition (BoD) of a matrix is obtained through Eigen Value Decompositions (EVDs) of its inner and outer squares. We compute the Eigen bases of input and output spaces using these EVDs, which is the building blocks defining their transformations. Imagine it as discovering the hidden blueprint that shapes the matrix's input and output

(a) Elliptic Paraboloid (b) Elliptic Contour (c) Parabolic Profile
Figure 49. Elliptic Paraboloid. (a) An oblique view shows the surface. (b) A top view shows elliptic contours of the surface. (c) A side view shows parabolic profile of the surface.

spaces! And here's the cool part: EVD provides a simpler way to understand these geometric concepts, similar to what we get from BoD, but presented in an easier-to-grasp way.

In practice, we want the unique solution even for singular linear systems. Here's a neat trick: we search for the closest determined linear system. In other words, we take the minimum-norm solution in the input space, minimizing error in the output space. For an underdetermined system, we select a solution with the shortest length in the input space. For an overdetermined system, we choose a solution that minimizes the error in the output space. The generalized inverse of a linear system ultimately leads to the unique solution.

4.1. Linear Least Squares

The squared error of a linear equation has the minimum value — zero — at the vertex of its parabola (see Figure 50). An error of a linear equation (7) or *linear error* is defined by

$$e(x) := b - ax. \qquad (104)$$

The graph of this linear error forms a straight line (see Figure 50a). The *linear error square* is nonnegative and reaches zero at its bottom when its slope, or derivative, becomes zero:

$$e^2(x) = (b - ax)^2. \qquad (105)$$

Visually, the graph of the linear squared error takes the shape

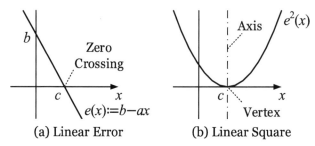

(a) Linear Error   (b) Linear Square

Figure 50. Linear Error and Square. (a) A linear error of a variable is a straight line on the coordinate plane. (b) The parabola of a linear square opens upward and varies in width.

of a parabola (see Figure 50b). A parabola looks like a curved U, varying in its width or steepness. It's symmetric around a special line called the axis of symmetry at $x = c$ and touches this line at a point we call the vertex of the parabola.

Here's where it gets even more interesting: minimizing a linear squared error is equivalent to solving a linear equation. When the derivative of this squared error is zero, it leads us to a linear equation so called *normal equation*:

$$\frac{d}{dx}e^2(x) = -2a(b - ax) = 0. \tag{106}$$

Expanding this equation gives us:

$$2a^2x - 2ab = 0. \tag{107}$$

If $a \neq 0$, $e^2(x)$ has the unique minimizer at the vertex c:

$$c = \frac{b}{a}. \tag{108}$$

If $a = 0$, all real numbers are minimizers of $e^2(x)$.

Moving on, if we extend this idea to several variables, the squared error of a linear system forms the shape of an elliptic paraboloid (Figure 51). The *error* of a linear system (74) is

$$\mathbf{e}(\mathbf{x}) := \mathbf{b} - \mathbf{A}\mathbf{x}. \tag{109}$$

The *linear error square* for this system has a quadratic form:

$$e^2(\mathbf{x}) := \|\mathbf{e}(\mathbf{x})\|^2$$
$$= (\mathbf{b} - \mathbf{A}\mathbf{x})^T(\mathbf{b} - \mathbf{A}\mathbf{x}) \tag{110}$$
$$= \mathbf{x}^T\mathbf{A}^T\mathbf{A}\mathbf{x} - 2\mathbf{b}^T\mathbf{A}\mathbf{x} + \mathbf{b}^T\mathbf{b}.$$

Now, the matrix square $\mathbf{A}^T\mathbf{A}$ decides the shape of the elliptic paraboloid (see Figure 51). Regardless of $\mathbf{A}$, its inner square is *positive semi-definite* because

$$\mathbf{x}^T\mathbf{A}^T\mathbf{A}\mathbf{x} = \|\mathbf{A}\mathbf{x}\|^2 \geq 0, \tag{111}$$

for all $\mathbf{x}$ (Figure 51a). The equality holds when $\mathbf{x}$ is a null vec-

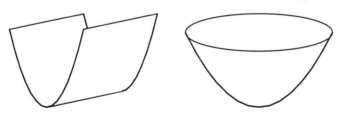

(a) Positive Semi-definite   (b) Strictly Positive Definite

Figure 51. Positive Definite Quadratic Forms. (a) A positive semi-definite quadratic forms has many minimizers. (b) A strictly positive definite quadratic forms have one minimizer.

tor of **A**. The matrix square is said *positive definite* if

$$\mathbf{x}^T \mathbf{A}^T \mathbf{A} \mathbf{x} > 0, \tag{112}$$

for all **x** except **0** (Figure 51b).

Minimizing a linear error square of several variables also becomes a quest to solve their linear system. We want to find the minimizer of the linear error square:

$$\mathbf{x}^* := \text{argument minimize}_{\mathbf{x}} \, e^2(\mathbf{x}). \tag{113}$$

And guess what? The linear error square hits its minimum value zero when its derivative with respect to **x** is zero:

$$\frac{\partial e^2}{\partial \mathbf{x}}(\mathbf{x}) = 2(\mathbf{A}^T \mathbf{A} \mathbf{x} - \mathbf{A}^T \mathbf{b}) = \mathbf{0}. \tag{114}$$

This leads us to a normal equation of several variables:

$$\mathbf{A}^T \mathbf{A} \mathbf{x} = \mathbf{A}^T \mathbf{b}. \tag{115}$$

Here's the exciting part: If $\mathbf{A}^T\mathbf{A}$ is positive definite, the normal equation gives us the unique minimizer of $e^2(\mathbf{x})$:

$$\mathbf{x}^* = (\mathbf{A}^T \mathbf{A})^{-1} \mathbf{A}^T \mathbf{b}. \tag{116}$$

But if $\mathbf{A}^T\mathbf{A}$ is singular, the normal equation results in many minimizers of $e^2(\mathbf{x})$ (Figure 51a).

Now, let's step into something called the *Lagrange multiplier method*. It's like unlocking constrained optimization problems, turning them into simpler, unconstrained ones (Figure 52). Let $f(\mathbf{x})$ be a differentiable objective function

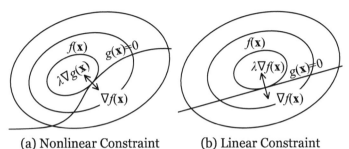

(a) Nonlinear Constraint   (b) Linear Constraint

Figure 52. Lagrange Multiplier Method. An equality constraint $g(\mathbf{x}) = 0$ tangentially touches a contour of a function $f(\mathbf{x})$ is the minimum of $f(\mathbf{x})$ along the constraint.

and $g(\mathbf{x}) = \mathbf{0}$ be a differentiable equality constraint:

$$\underset{\mathbf{x}}{\text{optimize}}\, f(\mathbf{x})$$
$$\text{subject to: } g(\mathbf{x}) = \mathbf{0}. \tag{117}$$

This equality constrained optimization is, in fact, equivalent to an unconstrained optimization of the Lagrangian function $f(\mathbf{x}) + \boldsymbol{\lambda}^T g(\mathbf{x})$ with respect to all unknown variables $\mathbf{x}$ and $\boldsymbol{\lambda}$:

$$\underset{\mathbf{x},\,\boldsymbol{\lambda}}{\text{optimize}}\, f(\mathbf{x}) + \boldsymbol{\lambda}^T g(\mathbf{x}), \tag{118}$$

where $\boldsymbol{\lambda}$ is the vector of Lagrange multipliers. Thus necessary conditions are obtained from the partial derivatives of the Lagrangian function $f(\mathbf{x}) + \boldsymbol{\lambda}^T g(\mathbf{x})$ with respect to $\mathbf{x}$ and $\boldsymbol{\lambda}$:

$$\frac{\partial f}{\partial \mathbf{x}}(\mathbf{x}) + \boldsymbol{\lambda}^T \frac{\partial g}{\partial \mathbf{x}}(\mathbf{x}) = \mathbf{0}$$
$$g(\mathbf{x}) = \mathbf{0}. \tag{119}$$

If the objective function is a linear error square function and the equality constraints form a linear system, (119) is necessary and sufficient conditions (Figure 52b).

4.2. Generalized Inverse

When we deal with singular linear systems, we want the best solution among many candidates. For underdetermined systems with too few equations, we pick the point closest to the origin — the *minimum-norm solution*. For overdetermined systems with too many equations, on the other hand, we pick the point with the smallest error — the *least square solution*. Both of these solutions minimize a squared error.

In an overdetermined system, the least square solution brings the smallest error in the output space. This system has a constant vector $\mathbf{b}$ in equation (74) lying outside its column space $\mathcal{R}(\mathbf{A})$, causing some errors in the output space (see Figure 53). In order to make this system determined, we find a point $\mathbf{p}$ in $\mathcal{R}(\mathbf{A})$ that's closest to $\mathbf{b}$. Let's assume for simplicity that the null space of $\mathbf{A}$ is trivial: $\mathcal{N}(\mathbf{A}) = \{\mathbf{0}\}$. According to equation (50), we can express $\mathbf{A}$' BoD:

$$\mathbf{A} = \mathbf{V} \begin{bmatrix} \mathbf{\Sigma}_r \\ \mathbf{0} \end{bmatrix} \mathbf{U}^T. \tag{120}$$

Since $\mathbf{A}^T \mathbf{A}$ is invertible, the solution from (116) looks like this:

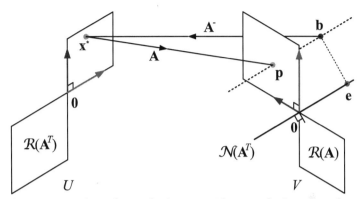

Figure 53. Action of Pseudo-inverse. The pseudo-inverse takes backward action to projects the constant vector **b** orthogonally onto the column space and find the least square solution.

$$\mathbf{x}^* = \mathbf{A}^- \mathbf{b}, \tag{121}$$

where $\mathbf{A}^- \in \mathbb{R}^{n \times m}$ is the generalized inverse of $\mathbf{A} \in \mathbb{R}^{m \times n}$:

$$
\begin{aligned}
\mathbf{A}^- &= \left\{ \left(\mathbf{V} \begin{bmatrix} \Sigma_r \\ 0 \end{bmatrix} \mathbf{U}^T \right)^T \left(\mathbf{V} \begin{bmatrix} \Sigma_r \\ 0 \end{bmatrix} \mathbf{U}^T \right) \right\}^{-1} \left(\mathbf{V} \begin{bmatrix} \Sigma_r \\ 0 \end{bmatrix} \mathbf{U}^T \right)^T \\
&= (\mathbf{U} \Sigma_r^2 \mathbf{U}^T)^{-1} (\mathbf{U} [\Sigma_r \ 0] \mathbf{V}^T) \\
&= \mathbf{U} [\Sigma_r^{-1} \ 0] \mathbf{V}^T.
\end{aligned}
\tag{122}
$$

A determined system has zero error in the output space.

For an underdetermined system, the *minimum-norm solution* is the one with the smallest length among all possible linear solutions. The solution set of an underdetermined system, for example, is a dashed line crossing a particular solution and running parallel to the null space (see Figure 54).

We want to find a solution with the smallest length among them all. It is a linearly constrained quadratic optimization:

$$\underset{\mathbf{x}}{\text{minimize }} \mathbf{x}^T\mathbf{x} \tag{123}$$

$$\text{subject to: } \mathbf{Ax} = \mathbf{b}.$$

Using the Lagrange multiplier method, the normal equations from in equations (119) are obtained by:

$$\mathbf{x} = \mathbf{A}^T\boldsymbol{\lambda}, \tag{124}$$

$$\mathbf{Ax} = \mathbf{b}. \tag{125}$$

By plugging (124) into (125), we solve a linear system for $\boldsymbol{\lambda}$:

$$\mathbf{AA}^T\boldsymbol{\lambda} = \mathbf{b}. \tag{126}$$

If $\mathbf{AA}^T$ is invertible, then the solution of (126) looks like this:

$$\boldsymbol{\lambda} = (\mathbf{AA}^T)^{-1}\mathbf{b}. \tag{127}$$

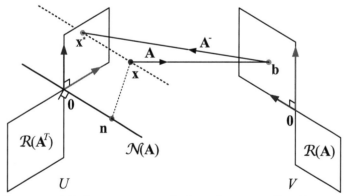

Figure 54. Minimum Norm Solution. The generalized inverse projects the general solution onto the row space and takes backward action to find the minimum norm solution.

By plugging (127) into (124), the minimum-norm solution is

$$\mathbf{x}^* = \mathbf{A}^T(\mathbf{A}\mathbf{A}^T)^{-1}\mathbf{b}. \tag{128}$$

Assume that the left null space of $\mathbf{A}$ is trivial: $\mathcal{N}(\mathbf{A}^T) = \{\mathbf{0}\}$. So, the BoD of $\mathbf{A}$ in equation (50) is specialized to this:

$$\mathbf{A} = \mathbf{V}[\boldsymbol{\Sigma}_r\ \mathbf{0}]\mathbf{U}^T. \tag{129}$$

Since $\mathbf{A}\mathbf{A}^T$ is invertible, the solution from (128) looks like this:

$$\mathbf{x}^* = \mathbf{A}^-\mathbf{b}, \tag{130}$$

where $\mathbf{A}^- \in \mathbb{R}^{n\times m}$ is the generalized inverse of $\mathbf{A} \in \mathbb{R}^{m\times n}$:

$$\begin{aligned}
\mathbf{A}^- &= (\mathbf{V}[\boldsymbol{\Sigma}_r\ \mathbf{0}]\mathbf{U}^T)^T\{(\mathbf{V}[\boldsymbol{\Sigma}_r\ \mathbf{0}]\mathbf{U}^T)(\mathbf{V}[\boldsymbol{\Sigma}_r\ \mathbf{0}]\mathbf{U}^T)^T\}^{-1} \\
&= (\mathbf{V}[\boldsymbol{\Sigma}_r\ \mathbf{0}]\mathbf{U}^T)^T(\mathbf{V}\boldsymbol{\Sigma}_r^2\mathbf{V}^T)^{-1} \\
&= \mathbf{U}\begin{bmatrix}\boldsymbol{\Sigma}_r^{-1}\\\mathbf{0}\end{bmatrix}\mathbf{V}^T.
\end{aligned} \tag{131}$$

This has a very similar structure with the generalized inverses of $\mathbf{A}$ for an overdetermined system in equation (122).

The generalized inverse of a linear mapping moves any vector in the output space to the least square and/or minimum-norm solution (Figure 55). It generalizes (122) and (131) for underdetermined and overdetermined systems:

$$\mathbf{A}^- := \mathbf{U}\boldsymbol{\Sigma}^-\mathbf{V}^T, \tag{132}$$

where $\boldsymbol{\Sigma}^- \in \mathbb{R}^{n\times m}$ is a diagonal matrix with reciprocals of the nonzero diagonal elements of $\boldsymbol{\Sigma} \in \mathbb{R}^{m\times n}$:

$$\boldsymbol{\Sigma}^- = \begin{bmatrix}\boldsymbol{\Sigma}_r^{-1} & \mathbf{0}\\\mathbf{0} & \mathbf{0}\end{bmatrix}. \tag{133}$$

So, the solution derived from this generalized inverse is

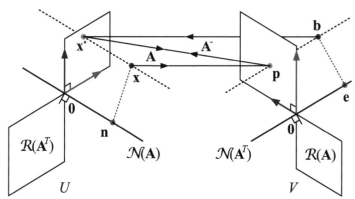

Figure 55. Action of Generalized Inverse. The generalized inverse embraces the pseudo-inverse and take the backward action to find the least square and minimum norm solution.

$$\mathbf{x}^* = \mathbf{A}^-\mathbf{b}$$
$$= \mathbf{U}\mathbf{\Sigma}^-\mathbf{V}^T\mathbf{b}. \tag{134}$$

Calculating the generalized inverse of a matrix is complex to characterize its backward action. Instead, we can consider its transpose that is algebraically lighter and shares the same range and null space as its generalized inverse:

$$\mathcal{R}(\mathbf{A}^-) = \mathcal{R}(\mathbf{A}^T)$$
$$\mathcal{N}(\mathbf{A}^-) = \mathcal{N}(\mathbf{A}^T). \tag{135}$$

The proof is obvious from BoDs of $\mathbf{A}$, $\mathbf{A}^T$, and $\mathbf{A}^-$ (Table 6). The eigenvectors corresponding to zero singular values of $\mathbf{A}^T$ and $\mathbf{A}^-$ are the same, meaning their null spaces are identical. Suppose $\mathbf{A}^-$ maps an arbitrary point $\mathbf{y}$ in the output space to

Table 6. Transpose and Generalized Inverse of a Matrix. The transpose and generalized inverse of a matrix have the same row and null spaces as in their BoDs.

Matrices	A	A^-	A^T
BoDs	$V \begin{bmatrix} \Sigma_r & 0 \\ 0 & 0 \end{bmatrix} U^T$	$U \begin{bmatrix} \Sigma_r^{-1} & 0 \\ 0 & 0 \end{bmatrix} V^T$	$U \begin{bmatrix} \Sigma_r & 0 \\ 0 & 0 \end{bmatrix} V^T$

a point in the input space, that is, $x = A^- y$. Then there is another point y' that A^T also maps to the same point x:

$$y' = V \begin{bmatrix} \Sigma_r^{-2} & 0 \\ 0 & 0 \end{bmatrix} V^T y. \qquad (136)$$

This understanding highlights that both forward and backward moves in linear mappings have similar structures in the grand scheme of Linear Algebra (see Figure 55). Ultimately, the transpose of a matrix is a simpler alternative to its generalized inverse, preserving the row and left empty spaces of the linear mapping and defining its backward moves.

4.3. Eigen Value Decomposition

Biorthogonal Decomposition of a matrix is obtained by two *Eigenvalue Decompositions* (EVDs) of its inner and outer squares. A linear transformation using the matrix square deforms a hypersphere centered at the origin into a concentric hyper-ellipsoid. For example, the inner square of A in (49)

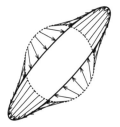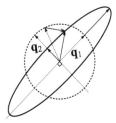

(a) Elliptic Deformation   (b) Invariant Axes

Figure 56. Positive Definite Linear Transformation. (a) A circle deforms into an ellipse by a positive definite linear transformation. (b) The linear transformation does not alter the orientation of vectors on the major and minor axes of the ellipse.

deforms a circle into a concentric ellipse (see Figure 56a):

$$\mathbf{A}^T\mathbf{A} = \frac{1}{4}\begin{bmatrix} 5 & 3 \\ 3 & 5 \end{bmatrix}. \tag{137}$$

A hyper-ellipsoids is specified by its principal axes and their respective lengths. The pairs of eigenvectors and eigenvalues of the matrix square determine these principal axes and their lengths of the hyper-ellipsoids, respectively (see Figure 56b).

A matrix square consists of nonnegative eigenvalues and orthogonal eigenvectors (see Figure 57). Consider a matrix square $\mathbf{S}$ of $\mathbf{A} \in \mathbb{R}^{m \times n}$ either the inner square $\mathbf{A}^T\mathbf{A} \in \mathbb{R}^{n \times n}$ or the outer square $\mathbf{A}\mathbf{A}^T \in \mathbb{R}^{m \times m}$. Let $(\lambda, \mathbf{q})$ be a pair of eigenvalue and eigenvector for $\mathbf{S}$, satisfying the following equation:

$$\mathbf{S}\mathbf{x} = \lambda\mathbf{x}. \tag{138}$$

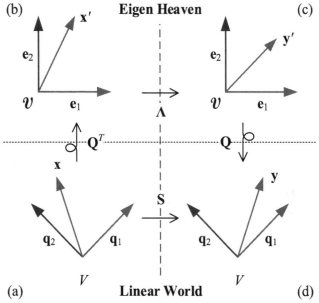

Figure 57. Eigenvalue Decomposition of Linear Transformation. A linear transformation is complicated in the linear world while its eigenvalue decomposition makes it easy via its Eigen heaven.

Thus, a diagonal and orthogonal matrices compose $\mathbf{S}$:

$$\mathbf{S} = \sum_{i=1}^{r} \lambda_i \mathbf{q}_i \mathbf{q}_i^T$$

$$= \mathbf{Q}\mathbf{\Lambda}\mathbf{Q}^T,$$

where $(\lambda_i, \mathbf{q}_i)$ is the i-th pair of eigenvalue and eigenvector, $\mathbf{\Lambda} := \text{diag}(\lambda_1, \lambda_2, \cdots, \lambda_r)$ is the diagonal matrix of nonnegative eigenvalues, and $\mathbf{Q} := [\mathbf{q}_1 \, \mathbf{q}_2 \, \cdots \, \mathbf{q}_r]$ is the orthogonal matrix consisting of the eigenvectors corresponding to the eigenvalues. All eigenvalues of the matrix square are nonnegative because it is positive semi-definite. The eigenvectors are orthogonal to each other, similar to the principal axes of the hyperellipsoid. Proof of this is left as an exercise for the reader. The direct action of the linear transformation is facilitated by biorthogonal bases (see Figure 58). Equivalently to equation (138), the following *Rayleigh quotient* is optimized:

$$\lambda(\mathbf{x}) := \frac{\mathbf{x}^T \mathbf{S} \mathbf{x}}{\mathbf{x}^T \mathbf{x}}. \tag{139}$$

Because the first derivative of the Rayleigh quotient with respect to $\mathbf{x}$ results in the equation (138).

Both inner and outer matrix squares share positive eigenvalues, where their corresponding eigenvectors span the row and column spaces of the matrix, respectively (see Figure 33).

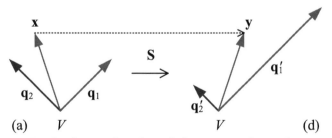

(a) V V (d)

Figure 58. Biorthogonal Action of Linear Transformation. Combining the second and third orthogonal steps, a direct mapping in the vector space with orthogonal bases is intuitive.

The inner square of a matrix $\mathbf{A} \in \mathbb{R}^{m \times n}$ comprises:

$$\mathbf{A}^T \mathbf{A} = \mathbf{U} \Lambda_n \mathbf{U}^T, \tag{140}$$

where $\Lambda_n \in \mathbb{R}^{n \times n}$ is a diagonal matrix of eigenvalues and $\mathbf{U} \in \mathbb{R}^{n \times n}$ is an orthogonal matrix where its columns are eigenvectors of $\mathbf{A}^T \mathbf{A}$. Similarly, the outer square of $\mathbf{A}$ comprises:

$$\mathbf{A} \mathbf{A}^T = \mathbf{V} \Lambda_m \mathbf{V}^T,$$

where $\Lambda_m \in \mathbb{R}^{m \times m}$ is a diagonal matrix of eigenvalues and $\mathbf{V} \in \mathbb{R}^{m \times m}$ is an orthogonal matrix with columns representing eigenvectors of $\mathbf{A} \mathbf{A}^T$. Let σ_i be the i-th singular value, the square root of the i-th nonnegative eigenvalue λ_i. From (138),

$$\mathbf{A}^T \mathbf{A} \mathbf{u}_i = \sigma_i^2 \mathbf{u}_i. \tag{141}$$

Suppose $\mathbf{A}^T \mathbf{A}$ is invertible ($\sigma_i \neq 0$ for all i) and define a new vector $\mathbf{v}_i$ such that:

$$\mathbf{v}_i = \frac{\mathbf{A} \mathbf{u}_i}{\sigma_i}. \tag{142}$$

By construction, $\mathbf{v}_i$ becomes a unit eigenvector of $\mathbf{A} \mathbf{A}^T$. Let $\Sigma_r := \text{diag}(\sigma_1, \sigma_2, \cdots, \sigma_r)$ be a diagonal matrix whose i-th element is σ_i. The relationships we have in matrix form are:

$$\mathbf{V} = \mathbf{A} \mathbf{U} \Sigma_r^{-1}$$

$$\mathbf{V} \Sigma_r = \mathbf{A} \mathbf{U}$$

$$\mathbf{A} = \Sigma_r \mathbf{U}^T.$$

Note that the first r columns of $\mathbf{U}$ form an orthogonal basis for the row space of $\mathbf{A}$, while the first r columns of $\mathbf{V}$ construct an orthogonal basis for the column space of **A**. In the low-rank scenario, some σ_i values could be zero. Provided the σ_i values are sorted, we can complete **V** by adding additional column vectors that span the output space $\mathbb{R}^m$ and then add rows of zero vectors to **Σ** corresponding to σ_i.

The *determinant* of a square matrix represents volumetric scale factor by its linear mapping. Importantly, the determinant of a singular matrix is zero. The determinant of **A** can be obtained by the recursive formula:

$$|\mathbf{A}| = \sum_{i=1}^{n}(-1)^{i+j}a_{ij}|\mathbf{A}_{ij}|,$$

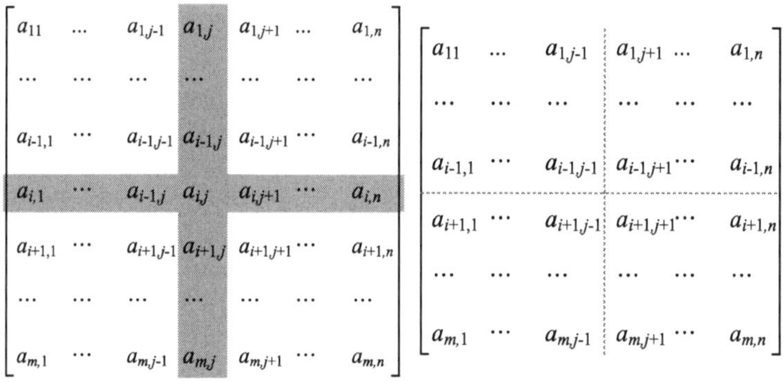

(a) Original Matrix   (b) Minor Matrix

Figure 59. Minor of a Matrix. (a) Elements on the i-th row and j-th column of a matrix are highlighted. (b) Elements on the i-th row and j-th column are eliminated in a minor of a matrix.

where $\mathbf{A}_{ij}$ be the minor of the entry a_{ij} in $\mathbf{A}$. The *minor* of an element in a matrix is the submatrix that results from crossing out the row and column of the element (Figure 59). For example, a minor of a 3×3 matrix is a 2×2 matrix:

$$\begin{bmatrix} 1.0 & 0.5 & 0.0 \\ 0.2 & 1.1 & 0.3 \\ 0.1 & 0.9 & 0.7 \end{bmatrix}_{12} = \begin{bmatrix} 0.2 & 0.3 \\ 0.1 & 0.7 \end{bmatrix}. \tag{143}$$

In two dimensions, the determinant is given by:

$$\begin{vmatrix} a_{11} & a_{12} \\ a_{21} & a_{22} \end{vmatrix} = a_{11}a_{22} - a_{12}a_{21}. \tag{144}$$

In three dimensions, the determinant can be expressed as:

$$\begin{vmatrix} a_{11} & a_{12} & a_{13} \\ a_{21} & a_{22} & a_{23} \\ a_{31} & a_{32} & a_{33} \end{vmatrix} = a_{11} \begin{vmatrix} a_{22} & a_{23} \\ a_{32} & a_{33} \end{vmatrix} - a_{12} \begin{vmatrix} a_{21} & a_{23} \\ a_{31} & a_{33} \end{vmatrix} \tag{145}$$

$$+ a_{13} \begin{vmatrix} a_{21} & a_{22} \\ a_{31} & a_{32} \end{vmatrix}.$$

Geometrically, the determinant of a matrix is the signed volume of a parallelepiped formed by the row or column vectors of the matrix (Figure 60). In one dimension, it is the signed length of a line segment (Figure 60a). In two dimensions, it is the signed area of a parallelogram (Figure 60b). In three dimensions, it is the signed volume of a parallelepiped (Figure 60c). In higher dimensions, it signifies the hyper-volume of a multi-dimensional parallelepiped. The right-handed rule on the vectors determines the sign of the determinant.

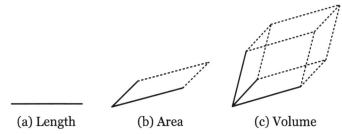

(a) Length (b) Area (c) Volume

Figure 60. Volume of a parallelepiped. The determinant of a square matrix is the volume of a parallelepiped induced by its row vectors. (a) The determinant of a scalar is the signed length from the origin. (b) The determinant of a two-by-two matrix is the signed area of a parallelogram induced by its two row vectors. (c) The determinant of a three-by-three matrix is the signed volume of a parallelepiped induced by its three row vec-

The characteristic equation of a symmetric matrix yields its eigenvalues. Let S be the symmetric matrix in d dimensions. If there is a nontrivial solution for (138) or

$$(S - \lambda I)x = 0, \tag{146}$$

then the characteristic matrix $S - \lambda I$ must be singular, resulting in its determinant being zero:

$$|S - \lambda I| = 0. \tag{147}$$

This equation is called the *characteristic equation* of S.

The Eigenvalue Decomposition (EVD) of a matrix square demonstrates how a linear transformation decomposes any vector into coordinates within its Eigen spaces, scales them within these spaces, and then composes the resultant vector. The characteristic equation of a symmetric matrix is a d-th order polynomial that has d real solutions. For example, $\mathbf{A}^T\mathbf{A}$ in (137) has two eigenvalues 2.0 and 0.5:

$$
\begin{aligned}
|\mathbf{A}^T\mathbf{A} - \lambda\mathbf{I}| &= \left|\frac{1}{4}\begin{bmatrix} 5 & 3 \\ 3 & 5 \end{bmatrix} - \lambda\mathbf{I}\right| \\
&= \frac{1}{16}(2.0 - \lambda)(0.5 - \lambda) = 0.
\end{aligned}
\tag{148}
$$

The EVD of $\mathbf{A}^T\mathbf{A}$ in equation (137) can be expressed as:

$$
\frac{1}{4}\begin{bmatrix} 5 & 3 \\ 3 & 5 \end{bmatrix} = \left(\frac{1}{\sqrt{2}}\begin{bmatrix} 1 & -1 \\ 1 & 1 \end{bmatrix}\right)\left(\frac{1}{2}\begin{bmatrix} 4 & 0 \\ 0 & 1 \end{bmatrix}\right)\left(\frac{1}{\sqrt{2}}\begin{bmatrix} 1 & 1 \\ -1 & 1 \end{bmatrix}\right).
$$

The determinant, eigenvalue, and eigenvector of a matrix are typically introduced first in Linear Algebra. They are very important stepping stones to see the orthogonal structure of a linear mapping. However, they do not convey the geometric intuition and algebraic ease required to grasp essential concepts in Linear Algebra fully. The book introduces the core concepts after Biorthogonal Decomposition. For those aiming to build a comprehensive understanding of Linear Algebra from scratch, several detailed books are available [1, 2, 3].

5. Linear World

Congratulations on mastering the Problem-Solving Trio with Linear Algebra! It includes three key notions: (1) relation, (2) analysis and synthesis, and (3) the split-solve-merge (SSM) method (see Figure I in Preface). You can address most problems by viewing how their parts relate and applying analysis and synthesis. Your attempts to break down a problem into parts, solve each part, and then build up a solution show your growth in problem-solving (see Figure 61).

The recurrent structure of the SSM method allows you to scale problems up and/or down. While solving a problem all at once might seem tempting, the SSM method offers clearer paths to finding a solution. Once you solve a problem, you'll

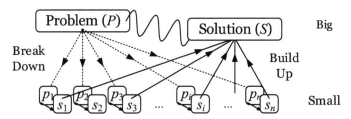

Figure 61. Problem Solving Diagram. A relational view helps us identify a problem (P) and its parts through repeated analysis and synthesis. The split-solve-merge method takes recurring steps to break the problem into smaller pieces (p_i), solve each piece (s_i), and then build up the big solution (S).

93

use it to address larger problems that include it. So, aim high with a big problem: apply analysis and synthesis repeatedly to its subproblems until the entire problem is solved.

Biorthogonal Decomposition (BoD) recaps both forward and backward actions of a linear mapping. The forward mapping computes the final result from its source by multiplying a matrix and vector, while the backward mapping finds a solution to a system of equations. BoD provides a unified tool to intuitively understand both forward and backward actions with orthogonal mappings — diagonal and orthogonal ones. Its SSM structure shows how to approach complex problems that go beyond linear mapping, which are nonlinear, infinite, and/or probabilistic (see Figure 62).

Piecewise linear approximation is a nice tool for handling nonlinear mappings in infinite dimensions. A vector in high dimensions can approximate a continuous function in space or time. With a discretization scheme, we can approximate a continuous function to machine precision. This embraces ordinary differential equations, partial differential equations,

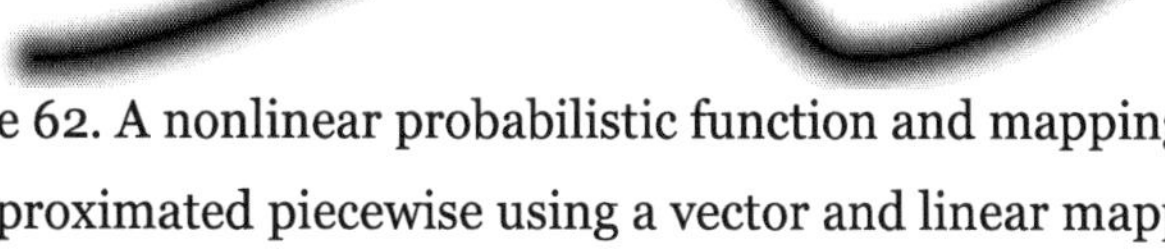

Figure 62. A nonlinear probabilistic function and mapping can be approximated piecewise using a vector and linear mapping.

and linear transformations such as the Fourier and Laplace transforms. Functional Analysis extends these concepts into infinite dimensions and shares similar principles with Linear Algebra. Specifically, spectral theory aligns with BoD.

Another nice tool is extending deterministic mappings to handle probabilistic ones. As quantum mechanics grew more important than classical mechanics, it's key to understand a probabilistic worldview alongside a deterministic one. In fact, a probabilistic state includes a deterministic one, just as particles can be understood in both ways. Linear filters are good examples of this extension.

Even history works much like science, inferring unknown stories from very limited observations using highly nonlinear probabilistic models. A historical problem is an underdetermined system due to incomplete observations. Some observations may even contradict each other, similar to an overdetermined system. Historians fill in the gaps with common sense, selecting among competing stories to tell a smooth one.

The linear world bridges the Eigen heaven and the complex world, applying problem solving methods everywhere.

6. References

[1] G. Strang, Linear algebra and its applications., 2006.

[2] G. Strang, Introduction to Linear Algebra, Wellesley-Cambridge Press, 2016.

[3] D. C. Lay, S. R. Lay and J. J. McDonald, *Linear algebra and its applications,* Pearson, 2016.

[4] W. Rudin and others, Principles of mathematical analysis, vol. 3, McGraw-hill New York, 1964.

A. Linear Axioms†

A.1. Field Axioms

Formally, the field is a set of numbers closed under addition and multiplication. It holds pairs of group axioms and the distributive law (Table 7). Here a, b, and c are elements in the field F, that is, $a, b, c \in F$. The first four axioms in pair are crucial for understanding algebra and geometry. Despite the four basic operations, addition and multiplication encompass the other two operations. In fact, subtraction is the inverse operation of addition, while division is the inverse operation of multiplication. The field is a formal structure that

Table 7. Field. A field is a set of numbers that holds the distributive law of two binary operations: addition and multiplication. $\ni$ means "such that" and $\exists$ means "there exist."

Axioms	addition	multiplication
closed	$a + b \in F$	$ab \in F$
commutative	$a + b = b + a$	$ab = ba$
associative	$(a + b) + c = a + (b + c)$	$a(bc) = (ab)c$
identity	$\exists 0 \ni a + 0 = a$	$\exists 1 \ni 1a = a$
inverse	$\exists (-a) \ni a + (-a) = 0$	$\exists (a^{-1}) \ni a(a^{-1}) = 1$
distributive	$a(b + c) = ab + ac$	

aligns with our algebraic and geometric intuition for these arithmetic operations. Refer to [4] for more on the existence of the real field $\mathbb{R}$ used in this book.

A commutative group is a set with a binary operation that satisfies the so-called "commutative group axioms." This commutative group is represented as $(G, \circ)$, where G is the set and $\circ$ is the binary operation. The five commutative group axioms include (G1) closure under operation, (G2) commutative law, (G3) associative law, (G0) identity element, and (G-) inverse element (Table 8). (G1) ensure that the set G is closed under the binary operation $\circ$:

(G1)   If $a \in G$ and $b \in G$, then $a \circ b \in G$.   (149)

(G2) ensures that the result is same regardless of the order of the two elements:

Table 8. Commutative Group Axioms. The five axioms of a binary operation are listed to be a commutative group.

No.	Axioms	Axiomatic Properties
G1	Closed	If $a \in G$ and $b \in G$, then $a \circ b \in G$
G2	Commutative	$a \circ b = b \circ a$ for all $a, b \in G$
G3	Associative	$(a \circ b) \circ c = a \circ (b \circ c)$ for all $a, b, c \in G$
G0	Identity	There exists $e \in G$ such that $a \circ e = a$
G-	Inverse	There exists $r \in G$ such that $a \circ r = e$

(G2) $a \circ = b \circ a$ for all $a, b \in G$.   (150)

(G3) ensures that the result is same regardless of the order in a sequence more than one operation:

(G3) $(a \circ b) \circ c = a \circ (b \circ c)$ for all $a, b, c \in G$.   (151)

Simply, we can denote them by $a \circ b \circ c$. (G0) ensures the existence of the identity element $e \in G$:

(G0)   There exists $e \in G$ such that $e \circ a = a \circ e = a$.   (152)

(G-) ensures the existence of the inverse element $r \in G$:

(G-)   There exists $r \in G$ such that $a \circ r = r \circ a = e$.   (153)

The inverse of a is commonly denoted by a^{-1}. For instance, the set of all integer numbers forms a commutative group under addition but not under multiplication.

Remarkably, the distributive law of addition and multiplication completes the linearity of multiplication in the field. In particular, it ensures the additive property of left or right multiplication in the field. The homogeneous property of left or right multiplication is derived from its associativity. The commutativity of multiplication guarantees that both left and right multiplications result in the same value.

A.2. Vector Space Axioms

Formally, a vector space over a field is a nonempty set of objects, called vectors, closed under vector addition and scalar

Table 9. Vector Space. The vector space is a set of vectors closed under vector addition and scalar multiplication that holds the following five properties in parallel.

Axioms	Vector addition	Scalar multiplication
closed	$\mathbf{a} + \mathbf{b} \in V$	$b\mathbf{a} \in V$
commutative	$\mathbf{a} + \mathbf{b} = \mathbf{b} + \mathbf{a}$	$[b\mathbf{a} = \mathbf{a}b]$
associative	$(\mathbf{a} + \mathbf{b}) + \mathbf{c} = \mathbf{a} + (\mathbf{b} + \mathbf{c})$	$(bc)\mathbf{a} = b(c\mathbf{a})$
identity	$\exists \mathbf{0} \ni \mathbf{a} + \mathbf{0} = \mathbf{a}$	$1\mathbf{a} = \mathbf{a}$
inverse	$\exists (-\mathbf{a}) \ni \mathbf{a} + (-\mathbf{a}) = \mathbf{0}$	-
distributive	$c(\mathbf{a} + \mathbf{b}) = c\mathbf{a} + c\mathbf{b}$	$(b + c)\mathbf{a} = b\mathbf{a} + c\mathbf{a}$

multiplication, with ten axiomatic properties (Table 9). Here $\mathbf{a}$, $\mathbf{b}$, and $\mathbf{c}$ are elements of the vector space V, that is, $\mathbf{a}, \mathbf{b}, \mathbf{c} \in V$, while a, b, and c are elements of the field F, that is, $a, b, c \in F$. The axioms of vector addition naturally extend those of scalar addition to multiple dimensions (Tables 7). Similarly, the axioms of scalar multiplication are extended from those of multiplication (see Table 10). The vector space axioms are, thus, multi-dimensional extension of the field axioms.

Consider an arbitrary number line passing through the origin. Let $\mathbf{e}$ be an arbitrary unit vector along the line. The real field along $\mathbf{e}$, $F_{\mathbf{e}}$, needs to adhere to axiomatic properties of multiplication on it. Here a, b, and c are elements of the

Table 10. Multiplication Axioms on a Vector. The multiplication axioms of a field on an arbitrary number line passing through the origin induce those of scalar multiplication.

Axioms	Multiplication on **e**	Scalar multiplication
closed	$ba\mathbf{e} \in V$	$b\mathbf{a} \in V$
commutative	$ba\mathbf{e} = ab\mathbf{e} = a\mathbf{e}b$	$[b\mathbf{a} = a\mathbf{b}]$
associative	$(bc)a\mathbf{e} = b(ca)\mathbf{e}$	$(bc)\mathbf{a} = b(c\mathbf{a})$
identity	$1a\mathbf{e} = a\mathbf{e}$	$1\mathbf{a} = \mathbf{a}$
inverse	$(a^{-1})a\mathbf{e} = 1\mathbf{e}$	-
distributive	$(b + c)a\mathbf{e} = (ba + ca)\mathbf{e}$	$(b + c)\mathbf{a} = b\mathbf{a} + c\mathbf{a}$

field $F_\mathbf{e}$, that is, $a, b, c \in F_\mathbf{e}$. To ensure all fields are identical in all direction, that is, $F_\mathbf{e} = F$, we use axioms of scalar multiplication. We want to ensure that **a** is a scaled vector of **e** by its isotropic magnitude a:

$$\mathbf{a} = a\mathbf{e}, \qquad (154)$$

Among axiomatic properties of multiplication along **e**, four axioms are reducible from $a\mathbf{e}$ to **a** in both sides and forms axioms of scalar multiplication. The remaining two axiomatic properties are always valid regardless of the field choice.

Index

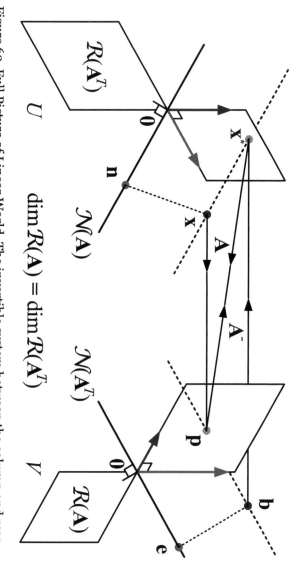

Figure 63. Full Picture of Linear World. The invertible system between the column and row spaces establishes one-to-one correspondences so that their dimensions are same. The column space is orthogonal to the left null space. So is the row space to the null space. The generalized inverse ($\mathbf{A}^-$) results in the least square and minimum norm solution if applicable.